Francesca Walsh and Kerry Young

ESSENTIALS

AQA GCSE
Biology

Contents

Contents

(N.B. The numbers in brackets correspond to the reference numbers in the AQA Biology specification.)

1. List A contains some lifestyle choices. List B contains some health risks.   (3 marks)

    Draw a line from each choice in List A to the associated health risk in List B.

    List A   **List B**

    | Eating a diet high in animal fats | | Heart attack |

    | Eating too much salt | | Liver disease | ✓ ✓

    | Eating too many high energy foods | | High blood pressure |

    | Drinking excessive alcohol | | Obesity |

2. Ron is overweight and wants to lose some weight. Suggest **two** things Ron could do to
    lose weight.   (2 marks)

    Exercise, eat less high energy foods ✗

    More exercise, intake less calories ✓

3. The following sentences are about cholesterol. Underline the correct words.   (3 marks)

    Cholesterol is made in the **pancreas** ✗ / **liver**.

    Inherited factors ✗ / **weight** can affect how much cholesterol the body makes.

    Eating **saturated** ✓ / **unsaturated** fats increases blood cholesterol.

4. Elena has an ear infection. She goes to the doctor. The doctor says she has a bacterial infection.

    (a) What treatment might the doctor suggest to kill the bacteria?   (1 mark)

    antibiotics ✓

    (b) Elena's white blood cells will help to fight the infection by engulfing and digesting the
    bacteria. Suggest **two** other ways that white blood cells help to defend the body.   (2 marks)

    Produce antibodies, produce antitoxins ✓

    (c) Dave feels unwell. The doctor says he has influenza, which is caused by a virus. He tells Dave to
    take some paracetemol or aspirin. Why would the doctor suggest this?   (1 mark)

    To relieve pain ✗ Alleviate symptoms of the flu ✓

5. Low carbohydrate, high protein diets are very popular with people wanting to lose weight. Scientists decided to investigate how the amount of protein in different diet plans affected the amount of weight lost.

This is what the scientists did.

- They found 100 obese people between 30 and 40 years of age and divided them into five equal groups.

- They gave each group a diet containing 1800 calories a day.

- They gave each group a different amount of protein in the diet plan. Similar foods were used for each group.

The average weight loss of each group after 26 weeks is shown in the bar chart below.

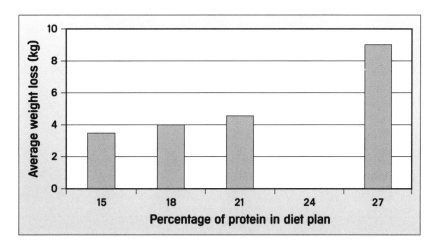

(a) The group with 24% protein lost an average of 6.5kg. Add this result to the chart. (1 mark)

(b) Give **two** variables that the scientists tried to control in this experiment. (2 marks)

1800 calorie diet, ~~amount of exercise~~ age 30-40 ✓

(c) Suggest **two** variables that the scientists did not control. (2 marks)

Amount of exercise ✓, gender ✓

(d) What conclusion could you draw from this experiment? (2 marks)

The more protein in a diet; ✓ the more weight lost ✓

6. When scientists want to study bacteria in the laboratory, they grow them on a soft jelly-like substance.

   (a) What is the name of this substance? (1 mark)

   _____

   (b) An inoculating loop is used to transfer bacteria. (1 mark)

   Why is the wire loop heated in the Bunsen flame?

   _____

   (c) After the bacteria have been transferred to a Petri dish, it is sealed with tape.
   Explain why. (2 marks)

   _____

   _____

   (d) What is the maximum temperature used in school laboratories to incubate the cultures of bacteria?
   Tick the correct answer. (1 mark)

   25°C ☐   **32°C** ☐   **47°C** ☐

7. In March 2009 a nine-year-old girl was found to be infected with a new strain of the H1N1 swine flu virus. Over the next few weeks many more people were found to have the swine flu virus and in April 2009 the World Health Organisation declared a pandemic.

   (a) Suggest how the new strain of the H1N1 virus arose. (2 marks)

   _____

   _____

   (b) What do we mean by 'pandemic'? (1 mark)

   _____

The graph below shows the number of reported cases of swine flu in the first ten days of May 2010.

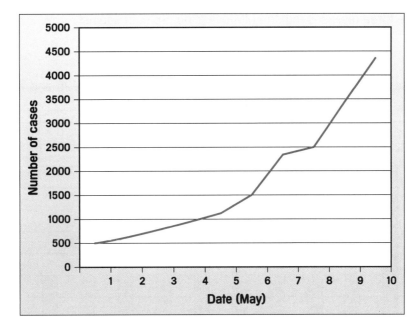

(c) How many cases of swine flu had been reported by 5th May? (1 mark)

(d) Which period showed the largest increase in the number of reported cases? (1 mark)

(e) Suggest why the spread of disease was so rapid. (2 marks)

(f) Why is it difficult to kill viruses inside the body? (2 marks)

8. Children are vaccinated against a range of diseases. Complete the sentences about vaccination.

Vaccines contain _____ pathogens. These stimulate the white blood cells to

produce _____. This results in the children becoming _____

to the disease. (3 marks)

9. The MMR vaccine was introduced in the UK in 1995.

(a) What are the **three** diseases that the MMR vaccine protects against? (1 mark)

The graph below shows uptake of the vaccine in the UK between 1995 and 2007.

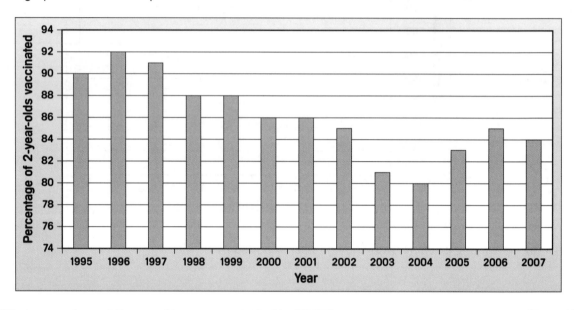

(b) What percentage of 2-year-olds was vaccinated in 2007? (1 mark)

(c) In which years was there a significant decline in uptake of the vaccine? (1 mark)

(d) Suggest a reason for the decline. (1 mark)

10. Complete the following sentences by underlining the correct words/phrases. (3 marks)

(a) A person is
| dehydrated |
| malnourished |
| anaemic |
if their diet is not balanced.

(b) A balanced diet should contain
| foods from each food group. |
| a mixture of fruit and carbohydrates. |
| no fatty foods. |

(c) Exercise will
| not affect |
| increase |
| decrease |
the amount of energy expended by the body.

11. Scientists often need to test bacteria for sensitivity to different antibiotics in order to decide the best antibiotic for treatment. To do this they spread the bacteria onto agar, which has been poured into a Petri dish and allowed to set. They then place small filter-paper discs containing different antibiotics onto the agar. The inoculated Petri dishes are incubated overnight and examined the following day.

(a) What is agar? (2 marks)

(b) The agar is heated to 121°C before it is poured into the Petri dish.

What is the reason for this? Underline the correct answer. (1 mark)

So it pours easily　　　　**To dissolve the nutrients**　　　　**To kill any microbes**

(c) Why are the inoculated Petri dishes incubated overnight? (1 mark)

(d) The diagram below shows the Petri dish after incubation overnight.

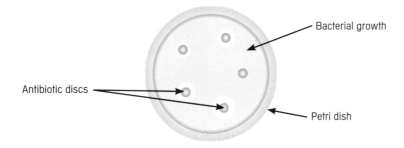

Erythromycin was found to be the most effective antibiotic. Penicillin had no effect at all on the bacteria.

(i) Label the antibiotic disc containing Erythromycin with an E. (1 mark)

(ii) Label the antibiotic disc containing Penicillin with a P. (1 mark)

(Total: .... / 49 marks)

12. Isoniazid was a drug developed in 1952 to treat tuberculosis (TB). Today one in seven new cases of TB is resistant to isoniazid.

(a) Explain as fully as you can **one** way in which this resistance could have arisen.   (4 marks)

_____

_____

_____

_____

(b) Nowadays it is common practice to treat patients with TB using two different antibiotics simultaneously. Explain how this can help reduce antibiotic-resistant strains emerging.

(2 marks)

_____

_____

_____

_____

(c) Doctors are concerned about the increase in the number of MRSA (methicillin-resistant _Staphylococcus aureus_) infections they are seeing. What can doctors do to reduce the likelihood of resistant strains emerging?   (2 marks)

_____

_____

(Total: _____ / 8 marks)

1. The body has receptors that respond to different stimuli. Complete the table below, matching the location of receptors to their stimuli. The first has been completed for you. (4 marks)

Receptor	Stimulus
Eyes	Light
Nose	**(a)** ....
(b)	Sound
Skin	**(c)** ....
Skin	**(d)** ....

2. The diagram below shows a reflex action.

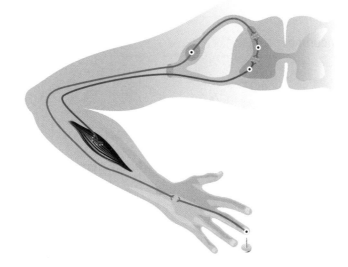

(a) Why does the body have reflex reactions? (1 mark)

....

(b) Draw **two** arrows on the diagram to show the direction of the nerve impulses along each of the neurones. (1 mark)

(c) There are three synapses on the diagram. Label any **two** of them with an **'S'**. (1 mark)

(d) Explain what happens at a synapse. (4 marks)

....

....

....

3. Identify the parts of the nervous system shown on the diagram. (3 marks)

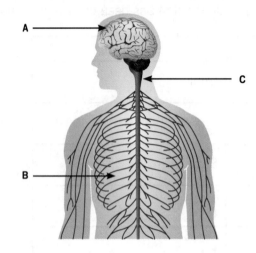

A ....

B ....

C ....

4. The diagram shows a neurone.

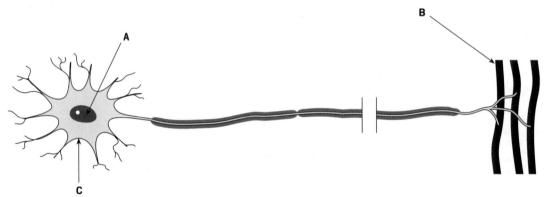

(a) Write the letter in the box that corresponds to the . . . (2 marks)

(i) Cell membrane ☐

(ii) Nucleus ☐

(iii) Effector ☐

(b) What type of neurone is this? (1 mark)

....

5. The following sentences are about hormones. Underline the word or phrase that completes each sentence correctly. (4 marks)

Hormones are produced by

the brain.
white blood cells.
glands.

They are transported to their target areas

by nerve cells.
in the blood.
attached to enzymes.

A hormone used in the contraceptive pill is

follicle-stimulating hormone.
progesterone.
testosterone.

A hormone given to women to increase fertility is

follicle-stimulating hormone.
progesterone.
testosterone.

6. Matthew shines a torch into Jayna's eye. He notices that the pupil in her eye gets smaller.

(a) Complete the sentences about this reaction, choosing words from the box below. You may use the words once, more than once or not at all. (3 marks)

eye	brain	nerves	light	reflex

(i) The stimulus is the ....

(ii) The receptor is the ....

(iii) The response is carried out by the ....

(b) What type of reaction is this? (1 mark)

....

7. *In this question you will be assessed on using good English, organising information clearly and using specialist terms where appropriate.*

A student germinated a bean seed. Diagram A shows the bean after seven days. She then turned the bean onto its side (diagram B). Diagram C shows the bean a week later.

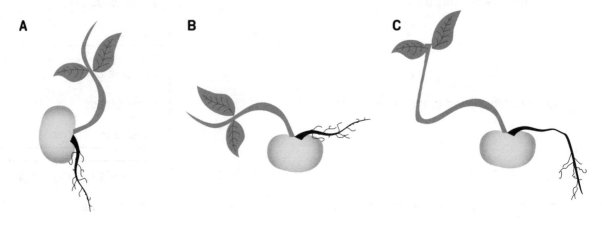

A   B   C

Explain fully why the plant responded in this way. (3 marks)

8. Read the following passage about *in vitro* fertilisation (IVF).

A woman unable to conceive may be offered IVF treatment. One cycle of treatment costs around £5000. Treatment involves numerous injections of fertility hormones so the woman will produce lots of eggs. Any spare eggs are destroyed. The success rate for one cycle of treatment is 28%. Doctors can now freeze spare eggs. If the first cycle of IVF is not successful, the frozen eggs can be thawed and used. Using frozen eggs costs around £1000 and reduces the need for repeated cycles of hormone therapy. Using frozen eggs has an 18% success rate. Some doctors are worried about the safety of using frozen eggs for the resulting children born, e.g. possible birth defects.

(a) Give **two** advantages of using frozen eggs. (2 marks)

(b) Give **two** disadvantages of using frozen eggs. (2 marks)

9. Ted uses 'ROOT-IT' to promote root growth in his plant cuttings. Bob makes his own rooting compound. He cuts some twigs of willow tree, mashes them into small pieces and leaves them to stand overnight in a tub of water. The next morning he removes the twigs and uses the water as rooting compound.

Ted and Bob want to know whose rooting compound is best. They take ten geranium cuttings each. They dip them in rooting compound and plant them. They measure the height of each cutting every four days. Their results are shown below.

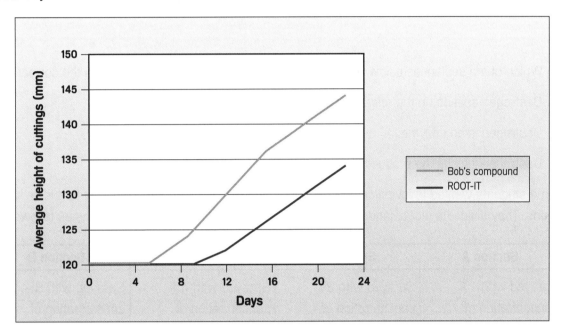

(a) Suggest **two** variables that Ted and Bob need to control to make the test fair.   (2 marks)

(b) What conclusion could you draw from Bob and Ted's experiment?   (2 marks)

(c) Suggest **one** disadvantage of using Bob's compound compared to ROOT-IT.   (1 mark)

(d) What is the substance present in both compounds that promotes root growth?   (1 mark)

10. The first contraceptive pills contained large amounts of oestrogen.

(a) Where in the body is oestrogen produced? (1 mark)

_____

(b) Nowadays, birth control pills contain much lower doses of oestrogen, which is combined with progesterone. Some birth control pills contain progesterone only.

Give **one** reason why the levels of oestrogen in birth control pills have been reduced. (1 mark)

_____

(c) Which of the sentences below about oestrogen is correct? Tick the box next to the correct answer.

Oestrogen speeds up the release of eggs. ◯

Oestrogen is an enzyme. ◯

Oestrogen inhibits the production of FSH. ◯ (1 mark)

11. Some students wanted to investigate the effect of using different concentrations of herbicide to kill weeds. They divided a plot of land into four equal sections and sprayed the sections as follows.

Section A	Section B	Section C	Section D
Sprayed with 1% concentration of herbicide	Sprayed with 2% concentration of herbicide	Sprayed with 4% concentration of herbicide	Sprayed with 8% concentration of herbicide

After a week the students counted the number of healthy weeds and dead weeds on each section. Their results are shown as pie charts.

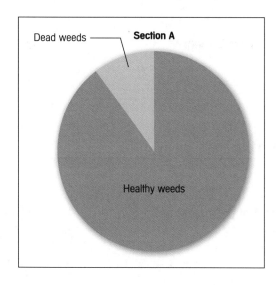

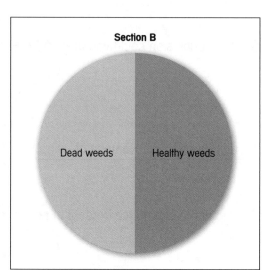

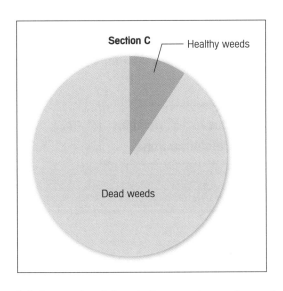

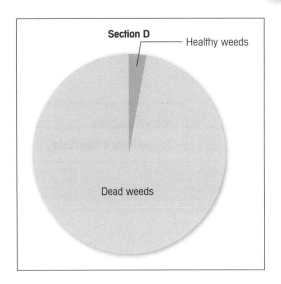

(a) Approximately what percentage of weeds were killed by the herbicide at 1% concentration? (1 mark)

(b) What concentration of herbicide killed most weeds? (1 mark)

(c) What concentration of herbicide would you recommend using? Explain your answer. (3 marks)

(d) Suggest **two** factors the students needed to control. (2 marks)

(e) Suggest a reason why weedkillers should not be used . . .

    (i) to kill weeds growing at the edge of a pond. (1 mark)

    (ii) to kill weeds in a hedgerow in the countryside. (1 mark)

12. The nervous system allows organisms to react to their surroundings.

(a) Put the following words in the correct order to show the pathway for receiving and responding to information. (3 marks)

relay neurone	response	stimulus	receptor
sensory neurone	effector	motor neurone	

....

....

(b) Where, in the above sequence, would you find a synapse? (1 mark)

....

13. Which of the following statements about plants are true? Write the letters of the **four** TRUE statements in the boxes provided. (4 marks)

A Plant shoots grow towards light.

B Plant shoots grow towards moisture.

C Roots have special cells called auxin cells.

D Roots grow in the direction of gravity.

E Plant auxins can be used as weedkillers.

F Plant auxins can be used as medicine.

G Geotropism is a response by the plant to the force of gravity.

14. It is important that the water and ion content of the body are controlled.

(a) Name the **two** ways that ions can be lost from the body. (2 marks)

.... and ....

(b) Name **one** other internal condition that must be controlled. (1 mark)

....

(Total: .... / 61 marks)

1. Listed below are four types of drug.

cannabis   **alcohol**   **statins**   **aspirin**

Write the name of **one** drug from the list that is: (3 marks)

(a) Illegal ....

(b) Legal and prescribed ....

(c) Legal and not prescribed ....

2. Complete the sentences below by filling in the missing words.   (4 marks)

Some athletes take .... to enhance their performance. These drugs are

.... by most sporting bodies. They are made from the male hormone

.... Misuse of these drugs may damage organs such as the

....

3. Some drugs are addictive.

(a) Circle **two** drugs from the list below that are most addictive.   (2 marks)

nicotine   **penicillin**   **aspirin**   **insulin**   **heroin**

(b) Explain why people who are addicted to a drug find it very difficult to stop taking the drug. (1 mark)

....

....

4. New drugs undergo testing before they are made available to the public. The steps below show the stages in drug development and testing BUT are in the wrong order.

(a) Put the five stages in the correct order by placing the correct numbers in the boxes. Stage one has been done for you.   (3 marks)

Trials using low doses of the drug on a small number of healthy volunteers	
Drug is passed for use by general public	
New drug is made in the laboratory	1
Clinical trials involving large numbers of patients and volunteers	
Drug is tested in the laboratory using tissue culture	

(b) Suggest **two** reasons why it is necessary for new drugs to undergo such testing.   (2 marks)

....

....

(c) In clinical trials, one group of patients is often given a placebo.

(i) What is a placebo?   (1 mark)

....

(ii) Explain why a placebo is given.   (2 marks)

....

....

....

5. Read the following statements about cannabis:

Cannabis use has been linked to mental illness.

Cannabis can be used to treat the symptoms of a number of diseases.

Cannabis is not addictive.

Cannabis may act as a 'gateway' drug to more addictive drugs such as heroin and cocaine.

Cannabis smoke contains around 400 chemicals.

Smoking cannabis is less harmful than smoking cigarettes.

(a) Choose **two** statements that could be used to support an argument for cannabis to be made legal.   (2 marks)

....

....

(b) Choose **two** statements that could be used to argue against cannabis being made legal.   (2 marks)

....

....

6. American scientists have recently suggested that a statin pill could be given to people eating in fast food restaurants to offset the increased risk of heart disease caused by the fat in cheeseburgers, fries and milkshakes. They suggest that the cholesterol-lowering drug, which costs only a few pence, could be handed out along with sachets of tomato ketchup.

Suggest **two** reasons why some scientists think this is a bad idea. (2 marks)

....

....

7. Thalidomide is a drug that was developed as a sleeping pill. It was found to help relieve the symptoms of morning sickness in pregnant women.

Explain why it should not have been given to pregnant women to treat their morning sickness.

(2 marks)

....

....

8. Statins are drugs prescribed to lower cholesterol levels in the blood.

(a) Why is it important to lower cholesterol levels? (2 marks)

....

(b) What might happen to someone if a coronary artery becomes blocked? (1 mark)

....

(c) Which organ of the body do statins act on? Underline the correct answer. (1 mark)

heart   pancreas   liver

9. It is estimated that the cost to the NHS of treating people with smoking-related illnesses is more than £5 billion each year. The cost of treating people with illnesses related to illegal drug abuse is between £3 billion and £4 billion each year.

(a) Explain why the overall impact of smoking on health is greater than the impact of illegal drugs. (1 mark)

....

(b) Suggest **one** social impact of drug abuse. (1 mark)

....

(c) Suggest **one** economic impact of drug abuse. (1 mark)

....

(Total: .... / 33 marks)

1. The illustration shows some adaptations of the polar bear.

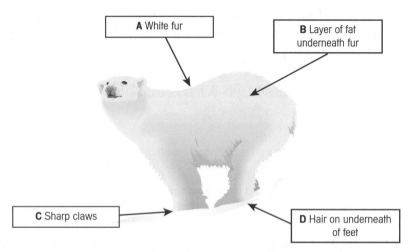

A White fur

B Layer of fat underneath fur

C Sharp claws

D Hair on underneath of feet

Match the adaptations to their functions by writing the correct letters (**A–D**) in the boxes below.   (3 marks)

For catching seals ◯

For warmth ◯

To help grip the ice ◯

For camouflage ◯

2. The Fennec fox is found in the desert.

(a) Suggest how the fox's ears help it to survive in its environment.   (1 mark)

....

(b) The arctic fox is found in cold, snow-covered areas.

Suggest **one** difference (other than ears) between the Fennec fox and the arctic fox that helps each to survive in their different environments. (1 mark)

3. The photograph below shows a red-eyed tree frog. These frogs are bright green with red eyes, blue stripes and orange feet. They live in trees in the rainforest and feed on small insects.

Explain how each of the following adaptations helps the frog to survive.

(a) It has sticky pads on its 'fingers' and toes. (1 mark)

(b) When sleeping, it hides its bright colours by closing its eyes and tucking its feet beneath its body. (1 mark)

(c) It has a long, sticky tongue. (1 mark)

4. Gurjot and Ben wanted to investigate the effect of grazing on the numbers and types of plants in an area. They found a field grazed by horses and used a metre square quadrat.

Gurjot suggested they place five quadrats in the field as shown in the diagram right.

Ben said they should place the quadrats randomly.

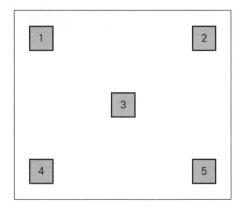

(a) Whose approach will give the most reliable results? (1 mark)

Gurjot and Ben counted the numbers of dandelion, dock and thistle plants inside each quadrat and found the mean average number of each type of plant per square metre. They repeated the experiment in another field grazed by sheep and a third field that had no animals grazing.

Their results are shown below.

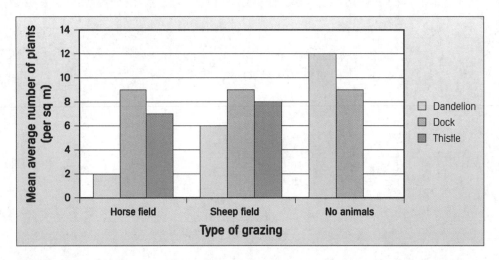

(b) The average mean number of thistles per square metre in the field with no animals was 7. Plot this result on the chart. (1 mark)

(c) Which field had the least number of dandelions? (1 mark)

(d) If the sheep field is 1000 square metres, calculate how many dandelion plants there are in the whole field. Show your working. (2 marks)

(e) What conclusions about the effect of grazing on plants could you draw from these results? (3 marks)

(f) Suggest **one** way in which Ben and Gurjot could improve the reliability of their results. (1 mark)

(g) Name **three** things that the dandelions, docks and thistles will compete with each other for. (3 marks)

5. The average daytime temperature in the Sahara desert is 45°C and it does not rain very often.

(a) Suggest **two** problems that animals living in the desert may have to deal with. (2 marks)

(i)

(ii)

(b) The cactus is a plant that is adapted to survive in desert environments.

Suggest how the following adaptations help the cactus to survive. (2 marks)

(i) The cactus has a thick stem.

(ii) The cactus has needles instead of leaves.

6. Scientists have discovered shrimps and giant worms that live clustered around hot vents on the ocean floor. These organisms can survive temperatures of up to 110°C. What name is given to such organisms? Underline the correct answer. (1 mark)

mesophiles   **gravophiles**   **extremophiles**

7. Dandelions, docks and thistles are all weeds and are well adapted to compete with other plants. The drawing below shows some features of a thistle.

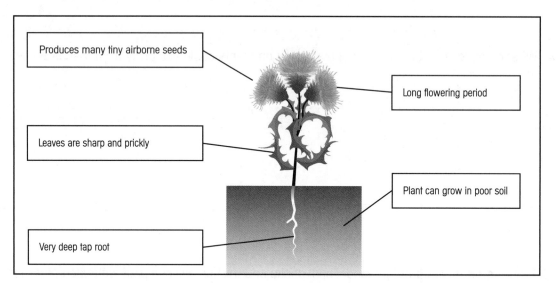

Produces many tiny airborne seeds

Long flowering period

Leaves are sharp and prickly

Plant can grow in poor soil

Very deep tap root

Choose any **three** of the above features. For each feature explain how it helps the thistle to compete and survive. (3 marks)

Feature 1: ....

....

Feature 2: ....

....

Feature 3: ....

....

8. Complete the following paragraph about measuring environmental change by filling in the missing words. Choose words from the list below. (3 marks)

oxygen   clean   polluted   indicator   gases   sewage   acid   microscopic

Some invertebrate animals, such as the stonefly nymph, are found only in streams and rivers

where the water quality is high. These invertebrates are called ....

organisms. The rat-tailed maggot can survive in .... water where the

levels of dissolved .... are low.

9. Bird populations are a good indicator of environmental sustainability and allow scientists to track environmental changes in particular habitats.

Scientists measured the numbers of farmland birds and woodland birds in the UK between 1972 and 2002.

Their results are shown below.

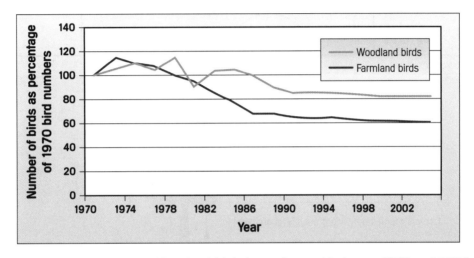

(a) Explain clearly how the numbers of farmland birds have changed between 1972 and 2002. (4 marks)

(b) Suggest a reason for the overall change in numbers of farmland birds. (1 mark)

(c) The government wants to reverse these changes by 2020. Suggest **one** thing it could do that would help to achieve this. (1 mark)

10. Suggest **two** factors that animals living in the same habitat will compete for. (2 marks)

11. Lichens are organisms that are sensitive to sulfur dioxide pollution.

Scientists wanted to investigate levels of pollution around an industrial area, so they carried out two line transects as shown on the diagram below. At 200-metre intervals along the transect they counted the number of lichens growing on the nearest tree, as shown in the diagram.

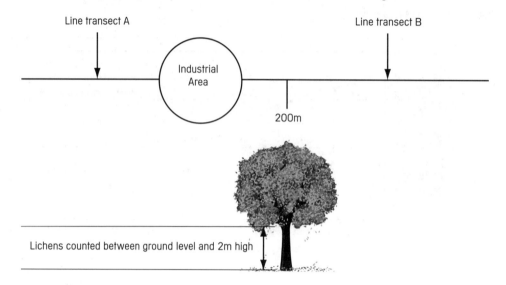

The number of lichens found are shown in the table.

Transect	200m	400m	600m	800m	1000m	1200m	1400m	1600m
A	0	0	3	4	5	8	9	8
B	2	5	8	9	9	7	8	9

(a) Suggest why the results for the two transects are different. (1 mark)

....

(b) What conclusion could you draw from the results of line transect A? (1 mark)

....

(c) Suggest why scientists did not count the number of lichens on the whole tree. (2 marks)

....

....

(d) Suggest **one** factor scientists were unable to control that could affect the reliability of the results. (1 mark)

....

(Total: .... **/ 44 marks)**

1. In an area of marshland there are numerous plants that are eaten by insects. The insects are eaten by frogs. Herons eat the frogs.

(a) Complete the pyramid of biomass by writing the names of the organisms in the correct places. (3 marks)

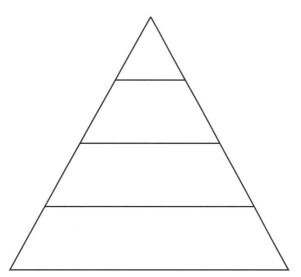

(b) What is the source of energy for all of the organisms in the marshland? (1 mark)

....

(c) Why is the biomass at each stage of the food chain less than the biomass of the previous stage? (1 mark)

....

....

(d) A farmer sprays a nearby field with pesticide. Some of the spray falls on the marshland and kills the insects. How will this affect the number of frogs?

Explain your answer. (2 marks)

....

....

2. The drawing below shows energy transfer in photosynthesis.

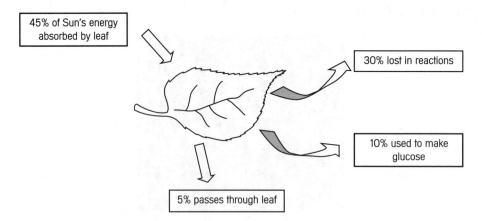

45% of Sun's energy absorbed by leaf

30% lost in reactions

10% used to make glucose

5% passes through leaf

(a) How much of the Sun's energy is used for growth by the leaf? (1 mark)

(b) A squirrel eats the leaf. The diagram shows the energy intake and output of the squirrel.

30% lost as movement

Energy in

20% lost as heat in respiration

40% lost through excretion (faeces and urine)

What percentage of the squirrel's energy intake is used for growth? (1 mark)

(c)   Use your answers from parts **(a)** and **(b)** to calculate what percentage of the Sun's energy is used by the squirrel for growth. Show your working out.   (2 marks)

(d) Suggest why it is more energy efficient to have a vegetarian diet.   (2 marks)

3.   The diagram below shows a food web for some animals that live on an allotment.

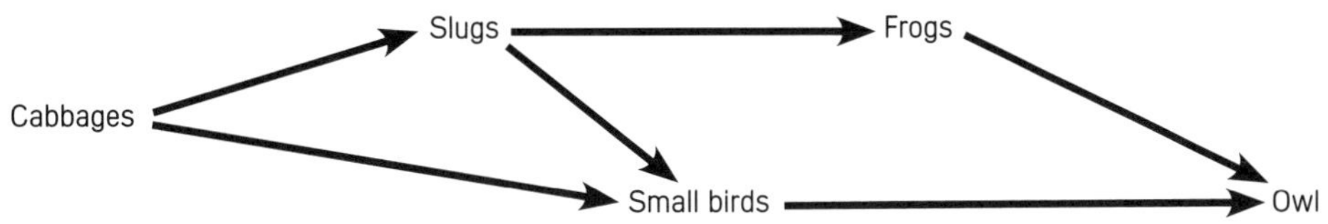

Suggest **three** reasons why only a small amount of the Sun's energy captured by the cabbage will be available to the owl.   (3 marks)

(Total: .... **/ 16 marks)**

B1 Waste Materials from Plants and Animals

1. Many people recycle their garden waste to make compost. This can be used to provide nutrients for growing plants.

   (a) The following list contains substances that can be recycled. Put a tick next to the **three** substances that could be put in the compost heap. (3 marks)

   Glass ☐

   Teabags ☐

   Grass cuttings ☐

   Tin cans ☐

   Vegetable peelings ☐

   Cooked meat ☐

2. Underline the correct word in each box below to complete the sentences about the carbon cycle. (4 marks)

   Plants and [animals / algae / fungi] remove carbon dioxide from the air.

   Plants use the carbon obtained to produce [glucose. / nitrates. / minerals.]

   When plants die, they are broken down by [consumers. / decomposers. / producers.]

   Bacteria and fungi are examples of [consumers. / decomposers. / producers.]

3. Jim, Robert and Harriet are all keen gardeners.

They make their own compost by collecting leaves from the garden and putting them in a heap.

Jim and Robert cover their heaps with thick black plastic to absorb the heat from the Sun.

Their compost heaps are shown below.

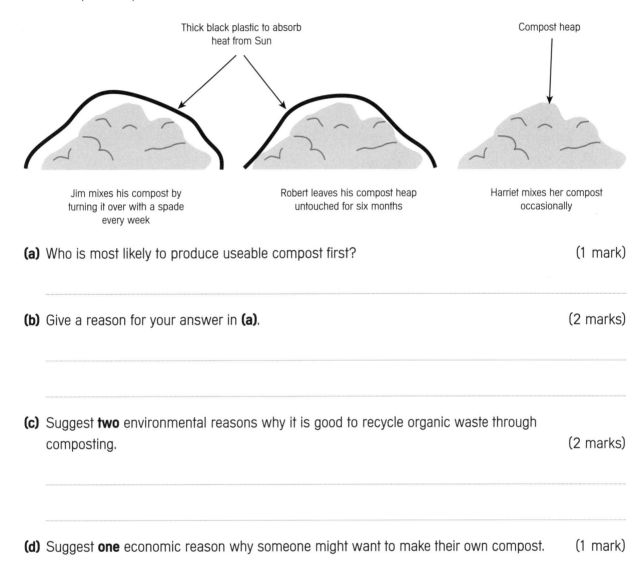

Thick black plastic to absorb heat from Sun

Compost heap

Jim mixes his compost by turning it over with a spade every week

Robert leaves his compost heap untouched for six months

Harriet mixes her compost occasionally

(a) Who is most likely to produce useable compost first?　　　　　　　(1 mark)

....

(b) Give a reason for your answer in **(a)**.　　　　　　　　　　　　(2 marks)

....

....

(c) Suggest **two** environmental reasons why it is good to recycle organic waste through composting.　　　　　　　　　　　　　　　　(2 marks)

....

....

(d) Suggest **one** economic reason why someone might want to make their own compost.　　(1 mark)

....

4. The diagram below shows some parts of the carbon cycle.

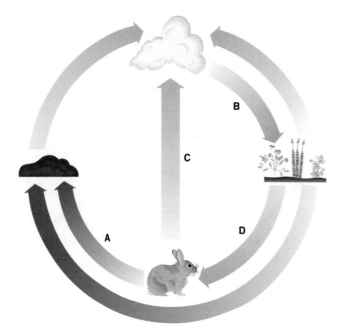

(a) Choose the letters from the diagram that correspond to the following processes: (4 marks)

Feeding ☐

Excretion ☐

Photosynthesis ☐

Respiration ☐

(b) Name another process, not shown on the diagram, that releases carbon dioxide into the air. (1 mark)

....

5. A group of students wanted to investigate factors affecting decay.
They mixed some soil with some small discs cut from leaves.

They divided the leaf disc/soil mixture equally into four test tubes as shown below.

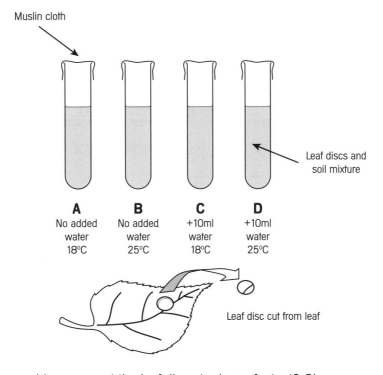

Muslin cloth

Leaf discs and
soil mixture

A	B	C	D
No added water 18°C	No added water 25°C	+10ml water 18°C	+10ml water 25°C

Leaf disc cut from leaf

(a) In which tube would you expect the leaf discs to decay fastest? Give a reason for your answer. (2 marks)

_____

_____

(b) The students did not add any microorganisms to the test tubes. Where will the microorganisms that cause decay come from? (1 mark)

_____

(c) Why did the students seal the tubes with muslin cloth instead of a rubber bung? (1 mark)

_____

(d) Suggest **one** way in which the students could use the leaf discs to measure the rate of decay. (1 mark)

_____

_____

_____

(Total: _____ / 23 marks)

B1 Genetic Variation and its Control

1. **(a)** Use the following words to label the cell below. (4 marks)

chromosomes   **nucleus**   **cytoplasm**   **cell membrane**

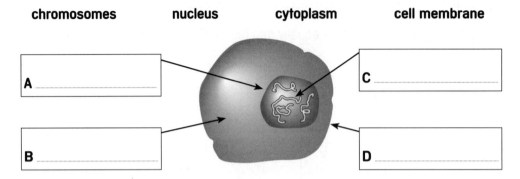

A ....

B ....

C ....

D ....

(b) Complete the sentences below by underlining the correct word in each box below. (3 marks)

Sexual reproduction is the
| division |
| separation |
| fusion |
of the male and female gametes.

The resulting offspring will contain
| DNA |
| cells |
| enzymes |
from both parents.

This gives rise to
| fertilisation. |
| differentiation. |
| variation. |

2. Below are some statements about genes. Some are correct and some are incorrect.
   Write the letters of the **three** correct statements in the boxes below. (3 marks)

   A Genes are sections of DNA.

   B Genes can code for proteins.

   C A sperm cell has 23 genes.

   D Genes are found in the cytoplasm of cells.

   E Genes are transferred to offspring only in sexual reproduction.

   F Chromosomes contain many genes.

3. Variation can be due to inherited factors, environmental factors, or a combination of both. Cathy and Drew are sister and brother.

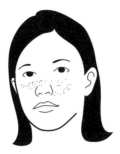 

The table below shows how they are different.

For each difference, complete the table to show if the difference is caused by inherited factors **(I)**, environmental factors **(E)**, or a combination of both **(B)**. (4 marks)

Cathy	Drew	Inherited (I), environmental (E), or both (B)
Freckles	No freckles	**(a)**
Long hair	Short hair	**(b)**
Good at music	Good at sport	**(c)**
Not colour blind	Colour blind	**(d)**

4. The diagram below shows the first stage in the process of insulin production using genetic engineering.

(a) What do scientists use to 'cut out' the insulin gene from the chromosome? (1 mark)

(b) The 'cut' gene is then inserted into a bacterium. Why are bacteria good host cells for the 'cut' insulin gene? (2 marks)

Genetic Variation and its Control

5. The diagram below shows the sequence of events used to clone sheep by embryo transplantation.

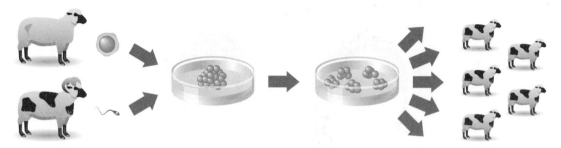

(a) Use words from the box to complete the sentences below. (5 marks)

gametes	old	implanted	shocked
directed	characteristics	sexual	wombs
asexual	sterile	stomachs	specialised

A male and female sheep with the desired _____ are mated. This is an

example of _____ reproduction. The embryo is removed from the female

before the cells become _____. The embryo is split into several clumps

which are then _____ into the _____ of surrogate sheep.

(b) Why would farmers want to use embryo transplants rather than waiting for the original
female sheep to give birth? (2 marks)

_____

_____

_____

(c) Explain why the offspring from the above process will be identical to each other but not
identical to the parents. (4 marks)

_____

_____

_____

(d) Scientists now have the technology to clone human embryos.
Give **one** medical reason why cloning human embryos might be allowed. (1 mark)

_____

_____

© Lonsdale

6. GM crops are made by cutting out desired genes from one plant and inserting them into another plant. Read the following statements about GM crops.

- GM crops give higher yields.

- GM crops might breed with wild plants.

- GM crops are insect resistant, thus reducing use of pesticides.

- GM crops can be enriched with nutrients, so are more healthy.

- GM crops may harm insects that feed on them.

- GM crops take up less land, leaving more for wildlife.

(a) Using the information above, suggest **three** reasons that could be used to support the development of GM crops.   (3 marks)

....

....

....

....

(b) Suggest **two** reasons why people are against the growing of GM crops.   (2 marks)

....

....

(c) Suggest **one** reason (not mentioned above) why scientists have developed GM crops.   (1 mark)

....

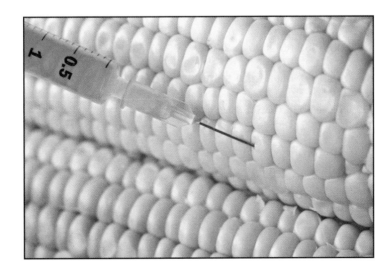

7. Adult cell cloning can be used to produce individuals with desired characteristics, e.g. good beef production in cows.

(a) The instructions below indicate the stages in adult cell cloning, but are in the wrong order. Put them in the correct order by numbering them 1–6. Two have been done for you. **(3 marks)**

The nucleus is removed from the egg cell. ☐

The embryo is implanted in the womb of another cow. ☐

The egg cell is fused with the body cell. ☐

A body cell is taken from a prize bull. ☐

The fused cells start to divide to form an embryo. **5**

An unfertilised egg cell is taken from cow B. **2**

(b) At stage 5, how are the cells prompted to divide? **(1 mark)**

---

8. Spider plants reproduce by producing stolons. This is an example of asexual reproduction.

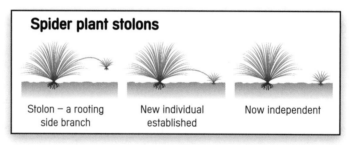

Spider plant stolons

Stolon – a rooting side branch New individual established Now independent

Circle the correct word from the pair given in the sentences below. **(4 marks)**

(a) Asexual reproduction needs **one / two** parent(s).

(b) Asexual reproduction does not involve production of **gametes / DNA**.

(c) The genes in the offspring will be **the same as / different to** the parent genes.

(d) The new plant is called a **shoot / clone**.

(Total: .... / 43 marks)

1. Many years ago, members of the giraffe family had short necks. The scientist Charles Darwin had some ideas about how organisms evolved. His theory suggested that some giraffes were born with longer necks, which gave them an advantage in finding food. They were therefore more successful and were able to breed and pass on their 'long neck' to their offspring.

Lamarck was another scientist with ideas about evolution. He had a theory that some giraffes grew longer necks to reach the leaves high on the trees. These giraffes were then more successful and were able to breed and pass their 'long necks' onto their offspring.

(a) Explain why Lamarck's theory is not correct. (2 marks)

....

....

....

(b) Darwin also suggested that humans and apes evolved from a common ancestor.
Give **two** reasons why Darwin's theories were not accepted by some people. (2 marks)

....

....

(c) How many years would it take for the short-necked giraffes to evolve into the modern giraffes of today? Underline the best answer. (1 mark)

five thousand   **five hundred thousand**   **five million**

2. The diagram below shows an evolutionary tree for some of our present-day vertebrates.

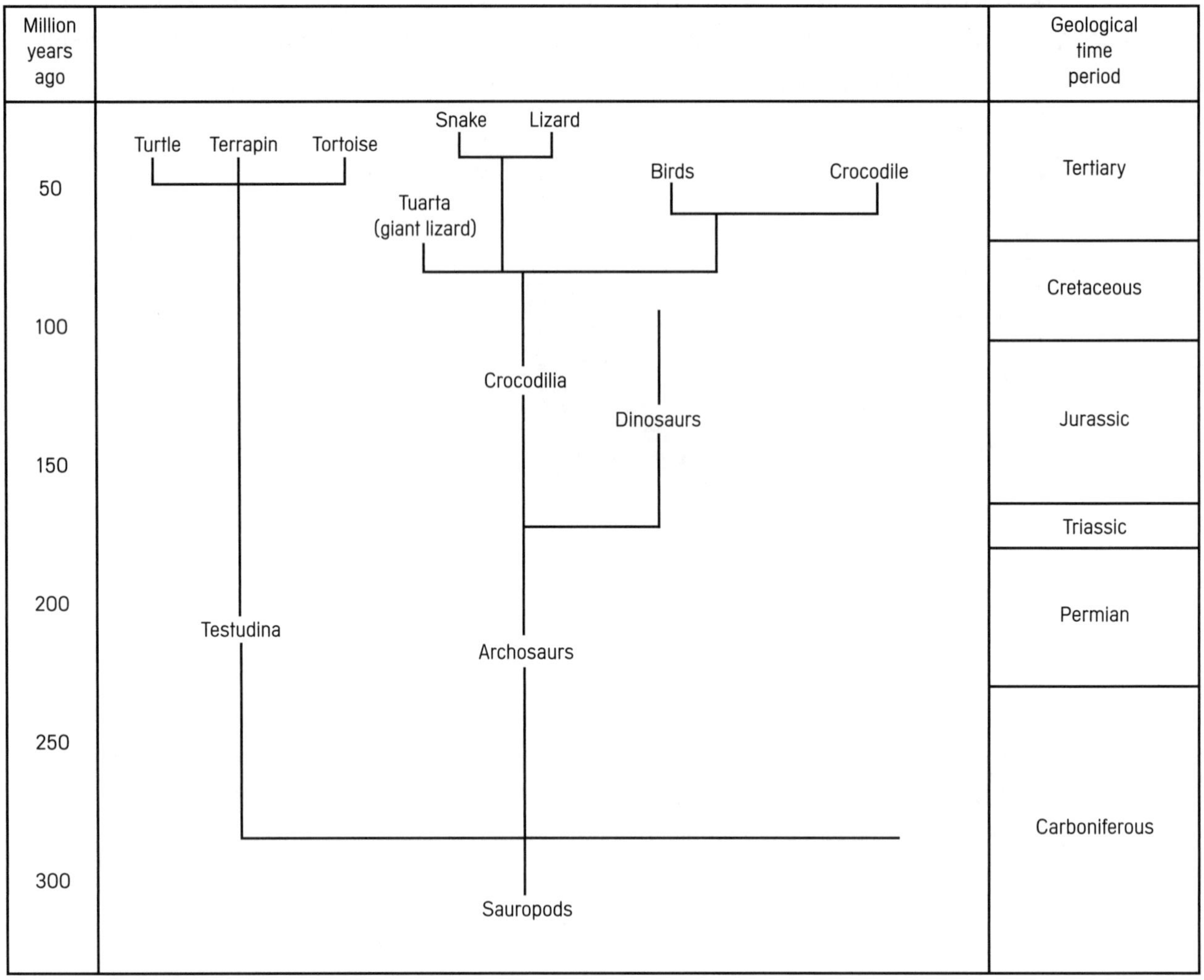

(a) How many millions of years ago did the testudina appear? (1 mark)

_____

(b) In what geological time period did the dinosaurs become extinct? (1 mark)

_____

(c) How do scientists know that dinosaurs once lived on Earth? (1 mark)

_____

(d) What group of animals alive today is most closely related to the snake? (1 mark)

_____

(e) Which ancestor is shared by dinosaurs, crocodiles and the giant lizard, but is not an ancestor of tortoises? (1 mark)

_____

3. Which of these passages describes the Theory of Evolution?
Tick the best answer. (1 mark)

Most species have been around since the Earth was first formed and
have changed to adapt to changes in the environment. ◯

Animals developed from insects approximately 200 million years ago.
Plants developed from organisms in the sea. ◯

All species in existence have developed from simple life forms
over a period of approximately 3 billion years. ◯

4. *In this question you will be assessed on using good English, organising information clearly and using
specialist terms where appropriate.*

Describe Darwin's theory of evolution by natural selection. (6 marks)

5.

Marsupials are a group of mammals that carry their young in the early stages of infancy in a pouch. The kangaroo and koala bear are examples of marsupials and yet they are very different. The koala bear spends much of its time climbing trees and has five fingers with short claws that grip the tree trunks. It spends up to 18 hours a day sleeping and is a solitary animal. Kangaroos are much more sociable and are found in herds. They have powerful hind legs and large back feet for jumping.

Scientists in Australia have recently discovered 26 fossils of an animal they believe lived 15 million years ago. The creature, which they have named Nimbaden, was about the size of a sheep with giant claws. The fact that so many fossils were found in one place suggests that Nimbaden may have travelled in herds. Some of the skulls found were of babies still in their mothers' pouches.

(a) Scientists believe that Nimbaden was a marsupial. Why do they think this? (1 mark)

....

....

(b) What fact suggests that Nimbaden may have been related to modern-day koala bears? (1 mark)

....

(c) In what way do scientists think Nimbaden was like modern-day kangaroos? (1 mark)

....

(d) What term do we use to describe animals that lived millions of years ago but no longer exist? (1 mark)

....

6. Scientists frequently study the distribution of the common snail, Cepaea. The snail has a shell that can be brown or yellow, and striped or unstriped. The shell colour and banding influences the visibility of snails to thrushes that prey on them. A recent study compared the distribution of snails in forest and countryside areas. The results, as a percentage, are shown below.

Area	Striped shell (%)	Unstriped shell (%)
Forest / woodland	13	87
Open countryside / hedgerows	75	25

(a) Suggest a reason for this distribution of snails. (2 marks)

(b) Which colour shelled snail would you expect to find most of in forest / woodland areas? Explain your answer. (2 marks)

Scientists also believe that shell colour influences the body temperature of the snails. Snails with dark shells warm up faster than those with light shells.

In cold areas, this would be advantageous to the dark-coloured snail.

The average annual temperature in Scotland is 2°C lower than in England.

(c) Where would you expect to find the highest percentage of snails with brown shells? (1 mark)

(d) Suggest what may happen to the numbers of brown and yellow-shelled snails if our climate continues to get hotter due to global warming. Give a reason for your answer. (2 marks)

(Total: .... / 28 marks)

1. Complete the table below with a tick (✓) or cross (✗) to show if the structures are present or absent in the cells listed. One has been done for you. (3 marks)

Structure/type of cell	Nucleus	Cytoplasm	Cell membrane	Cell wall
Plant cell				
Bacterial cell	✗			
Animal cell				

2. Some cells are specialised to carry out a specific function. Match the cell descriptions in List A to the corresponding functions in List B. In each case, draw a line between the two. (3 marks)

List A

| The cell has hair-like structures |
| The cell is very large |
| This cell has a tail |
| This cell can be very long with branched endings |

List B

| To act as a food supply |
| To carry nerve impulses |
| To absorb water |
| To swim |

3. The drawing shows a specialised cell.

(a) What is the name of this cell? (1 mark)

_____

(b) Suggest a reason why this cell does not have a nucleus. (1 mark)

_____

_____

4. Fiona and Issac are studying a diagram of a single-celled organism called Euglena.

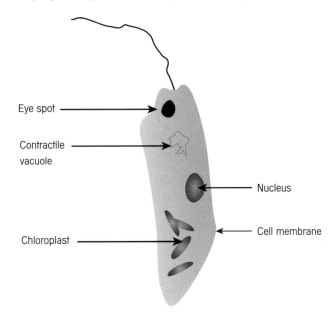

Eye spot

Contractile
vacuole

Nucleus

Cell membrane

Chloroplast

(a) Fiona thinks Euglena is a plant cell. Give **one** reason why she might think this. (1 mark)

(b) Issac says that Euglena cannot be a plant cell. Suggest **one** reason why he says this. (1 mark)

5. Complete the sentences below about the different parts of a cell by underlining the correct word in each of the boxes. (3 marks)

(a) Most of the chemical reactions in a cell take place in the

| cell membrane. |
| cytoplasm. |
| vacuole. |

(b) Energy from respiration is released in the

| cytoplasm. |
| cell wall. |
| mitochondria. |

(c) Proteins are synthesised at the

| chloroplasts. |
| ribosomes. |
| mitochondria. |

6. The diagram below shows a single-celled organism called an amoeba.

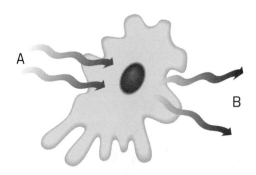

Substances pass in and out of the amoeba by diffusion.

(a) Suggest **two** substances that could be represented by arrows A. (2 marks)

_____ and _____

(b) Suggest **two** substances that could be represented by arrows B. (2 marks)

_____ and _____

7. Some students set up an experiment to investigate diffusion. They made a model cell using an artificial membrane that allowed small molecules such as water and glucose to pass through. They filled the cell with pure water and placed it in a solution containing glucose. They measured the concentration of glucose inside the cell every 20 minutes.

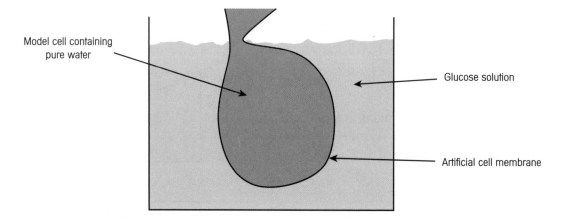

Their results are shown on the graph below.

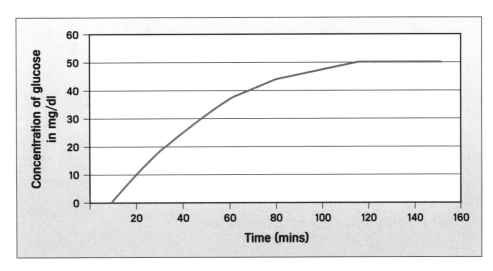

(a) What was the concentration of glucose inside the cell after 40 minutes? (1 mark)

.

(b) Describe what the graph is showing. (2 marks)

(c) Explain what is happening. (3 marks)

(d) Why does the process appear to stop after 120 minutes? (1 mark)

8. Complete the sentences below about diffusion by inserting the correct words. (4 marks)

Diffusion is the spreading of .... or any substances in a solution from an area

of .... concentration to an area of .... concentration.

The greater the difference in concentration, the .... the rate of diffusion.

9. The diagram shows a palisade cell.

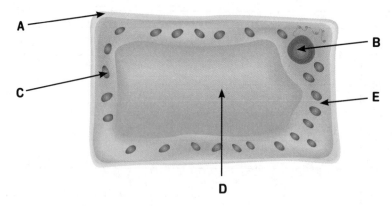

(a) In which part of a plant would you find a palisade cell? (1 mark)

....

(b) Which structures **(A–E)** match the following descriptions? Write the correct letter in each box.
You may use the same letter more than once. (8 marks)

Where most chemical reactions take place ☐

Made of cellulose ☐

Contains chlorophyll ☐

Controls what the cell does ☐

Gives the cell rigidity and strength ☐

Filled with cell sap ☐

Where photosynthesis occurs ☐

Contains chromosomes ☐

10. The sentences below are about bacterial cells. Circle the correct words from each pair. (4 marks)

A bacterial cell consists of **cytoplasm / cytotoxin** surrounded by a cell membrane.

Outside the cell membrane is a **cell wall / guard cell**.

The cell walls in bacteria and plants are made of **the same substance / different substances**.

The genetic material in bacteria is found **in a nucleus / free within the cell**.

(Total: .... / 41 marks)

AQA GCSE Biology Workbook Answers

Keeping Healthy (pp 4–10)

1. Eating a diet high in animal fats — Heart attack
   Eating too much salt — High blood pressure
   Eating too many high energy foods — Obesity
   Drinking excessive alcohol — Liver disease
   (*1 correct = 1 mark; 2 correct = 2 marks; All 4 correct = 3 marks*)

2. Reduce his calorie intake; Increase the amount of exercise he does.

3. liver; inherited factors; saturated

4. **(a)** Antibiotics
   (b) Produce antibodies; Produce antitoxins.
   (c) To alleviate the symptoms of the flu.

5. **(a)**

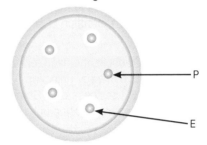

   (b) Any two from: Age group of people; All obese; Daily calorie intake; Similar foods
   (c) Any two from: Sex of group; How obese they were; Amount of exercise taken
   (d) The higher the amount of protein in a diet plan; the more weight is likely to be lost.

6. **(a)** Agar
   (b) To sterilise it/kill any microbes on it.
   (c) To prevent microbes from the air getting in; to prevent possible harmful organisms getting out.
   (d) 25°C

7. **(a)** It had arisen from a mutation; of an older strain of the virus.
   (b) A disease that has travelled between countries.
   (c) 1300
   (d) 8–10th May
   (e) People were not immune; There was no vaccine available.
   (f) They are found in cells; and treatment often damages the body's cells.

8. dead/weakened; antibodies; immune

9. **(a)** Mumps, measles, rubella
   (b) 84%
   (c) 2003–2004
   (d) Accept one from: Loss of public confidence about the safety of the vaccination; Reports about a possible link between the MMR vaccine and autism.

10. **(a)** malnourished
    (b) foods from each food group.
    (c) increase

11. **(a)** A jelly-like substance containing nutrients; that bacteria need to grow/A culture medium
    (b) To kill any microbes.
    (c) So the bacteria will grow.
    (d) (i) and **(ii)** See diagram below.

12. **(a)** Within the population of TB bacteria there may be a few organisms with natural resistance to isoniazid; This could be a result of a mutation; When a patient is treated with isoniazid, all the sensitive bacteria are killed; This allows resistant bacteria to quickly grow and multiply.
    (b) If a bacterium develops resistance to one of the antibiotics; it will still be killed by the second antibiotic.
    (c) Not overprescribe antibiotics; Not use antibiotics to treat minor infections.

Nerves and Hormones (pp 11–18)

1. **(a)** Smell
   (b) Ears
   (c–d) Any two from: Touch; Temperature; Pain; Pressure

2. **(a)** To protect itself
   (b–c)

   (d) When the electrical impulse reaches the synapse, a chemical transmitter substance is released by the first neurone; The transmitter activates receptors on the second neurone; causing a new electrical impulse to be generated in the second neurone; The transmitter is then destroyed.

3. **(A)** brain
   (B) spinal nerves
   (C) spinal cord

4. **(a) (i)** C
   (ii) A
   (iii) B (*1 correct = 1 mark; All correct = 2 marks*)
   (b) motor neurone

5. glands; in the blood; progesterone; follicle-stimulating hormone

6. **(a) (i)** light
   (ii) eye
   (iii) eye
   (b) Reflex

7. **This is a model answer that would score full marks.** The shoot will always grow upwards against the direction of gravity and the roots will always grow downwards in the direction of gravity. This is called geotropism.

8. **(a)** It is cheaper; It reduces the need for repeated cycles of hormone therapy (injections).
   (b) It only has an 18% success rate; Some doctors worry about the safety of using eggs for the children born.

9. **(a) Any two from:** Amount of water; Amount of light; Temperature; Size of cuttings at start.
   (b) Bob's rooting compound makes the roots grow faster; so the plants themselves grow faster.
   (c) Any of the following: Willow tree twigs may be difficult to find; It takes a lot of time to make the compound; The compound might not keep for very long.
   (d) auxin

10. **(a)** ovaries
    (b) People taking oestrogen pills experienced unpleasant side-effects.
    (c) Oestrogen inhibits the production of FSH.

11. **(a)** Accept any answer between 10% and 15%
    (b) 8%
    (c) 4%; Kills nearly all weeds; Will be cheaper than 8%; Twice as much weedkiller will mean more damage to environment.
    (d) Any two from: Type of weeds in the land; Amount of weedkiller used, e.g. application rate; Aspect of land, e.g. shade/sun.
    (e) (i) They may get into the pond and harm aquatic life, e.g. water creatures.
    (ii) They may kill the hedge (which is a habitat for many organisms).

12. **(a)** stimulus, receptor, sensory neurone, relay neurone, motor neurone, effector, response
    (*All correct = 3 marks, 4 or more in correct order = 2 marks, stimulus at start and response at end = 1 mark*).
    (b) Between sensory neurone and relay neurone; Between relay neurone and motor neurone (*either answer correct*).

13. A; D; E; G

14. **(a)** In sweat; In urine
    (b) One of the following: Temperature; Blood glucose/sugar levels

The Use and Abuse of Drugs (pp 19–21)

1. **(a)** Cannabis
   (b) Statins/aspirin
   (c) Alcohol/aspirin

2. anabolic steroids; banned; testosterone; heart/liver.

3. **(a)** nicotine; heroin
   (b) Accept one from: Drugs alter the body's chemistry; People get withdrawal symptoms.

4. **(a) 1.** New drug is made in the laboratory.
   2. Drug is tested in the laboratory using tissue culture.
   3. Trials using low doses of drug on a small number of healthy volunteers.
   4. Clinical trials involving large numbers of patients and volunteers.
   5. Drug is passed for use by general public.
   (*All 4 correct = 3 marks; 3 correct = 2 marks; 2 correct = 1 mark*)
   (b) To check for toxicity (they are not harmful); To check for efficacy (they work).
   (c) (i) A dummy drug
   (ii) The group given the placebo will act as a control group; The effect of any drug can be compared against people not taking the drug.

5. **(a) Any two from:** Cannabis can be used to treat the symptoms of a number of diseases; Cannabis is not addictive; Smoking cannabis is less harmful than smoking cigarettes.
   (b) Any two from: Cannabis use has been linked to mental illness; Cannabis may act as a 'gateway' drug to more addictive drugs such as heroin and cocaine; Cannabis smoke contains around 400 chemicals.

6. **Any two from:** This could be seen as encouraging people to eat high fat foods; High cholesterol is only one problem caused by high fat diets; A statin pill will not protect against other problems caused by a high fat diet, e.g. obesity; Statins need to be taken regularly to be effective; Statins can have side-effects.

7. **Any two from:** It had not been tested as treatment for morning sickness; It had not been tested on pregnant women; It could harm the unborn baby.

8. **(a)** Cholesterol builds up in arteries that take blood to heart muscle; Can cause narrowing of arteries/heart disease.
   (b) Heart attack/chest pains/shortness of breath
   (c) liver

9. **(a)** Far more people smoke than use illegal drugs.
   (b) One of the following: Crime – people steal to get money to buy drugs; Family breakdown
   (c) One of the following: People unable to work; People claiming benefits because they cannot work; Cost to justice system in dealing with crime.

Interdependence and Adaptation (pp 22–28)

1. For catching seals – C
   For warmth – B
   To help grip the ice – D
   For camouflage – A
   (*1 correct = 1 mark; 2 correct = 2 marks; All 4 correct = 3 marks*)

2. **(a)** They present a large surface area for blood to flow through and lose heat.
   (b) One of the following: Colour of fur; Thickness of fur; Amount of fat.

3. **(a)** Allow it to grip/stick to trees.
   (b) Camouflage so it won't be seen.
   (c) To catch insects/prey.

4. **(a)** Ben's
   (b)
   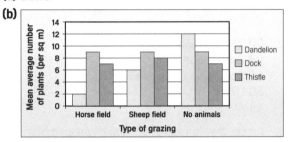
   (c) Horse field
   (d) 6 × 1000; = 6000
   (e) Both horses and sheep eat dandelions; Horses eat more dandelions than sheep; Neither horses nor sheep graze on dock or thistles.
   (f) Any one from: They could take more quadrats; They could repeat the experiment on a different piece of land; They could repeat investigation at different times of year
   (g) Any three from: Light; Space; Water; Nutrients

5. **(a) (i-ii)** Very high temperatures; Very little water to drink
   (b) (i) This stores water
   (ii) This reduces the amount of water the cactus loses through its leaves

6. extremophiles

7. **Any three from:** Many tiny airborne seeds – seeds can be carried a long way and even if many die, plenty will grow into adult plants; Sharp, prickly leaves – this will deter animals from eating the thistle; Very deep tap root – allows plant to get more water/makes it difficult to pull up; Long flowering period – plenty of opportunity for insects to pollinate plants; Plant can grow in poor soil – it can grow where other plants might not be able to.

8. indicator; polluted; oxygen

9. **(a)** There was a slight rise in 1974; But since then the numbers have decreased rapidly between 1976 and 1986; And decreased slowly between 1986 and 2002 (*1 mark for dates*)
   (b) Farmers have cut down hedgerows and/or trees so the birds have had nowhere to nest and their food source has been reduced.

(c) Any of the following: Plant more trees; Encourage farmers to plant hedgerows; Encourage farmers to leave field edges wild as food for birds; Use fewer pesticides

10. **Any two from:** Food; Mates; Territory

11. **(a) Any one from:** The direction of the wind; Transect A may have passed over more roads, which could have caused increased pollution/sulfur dioxide levels.
    (b) The industrial area was producing sulfur dioxide pollution.
    (c) The trees would have been different heights; This would affect the reliability of the data.
    (d) Any one from: Width of tree trunks; Distance of nearest tree to transect; Type of tree.

Energy and Biomass in Food Chains (pp 29–31)

1. **(a)** Heron
   Frog
   Insect
   Marsh plants
   (*1 correct = 1 mark; 2 correct = 2 marks; All 4 correct = 3 marks*)
   (b) the Sun
   (c) Energy is lost at every stage (trophic level) of the food chain and therefore there is less energy available for growth.
   (d) The number of frogs will decrease; Because they have less food.

2. **(a)** 10%
   (b) 10%
   (c) 10% of 10% = 0.1 × 0.1; = 0.01 = 1%
   (d) All of the energy in the vegetable gets passed on to the human in a vegetarian diet; If the vegetable is eaten by an animal, when the animal is eaten by a human, the human will only get a tenth of the energy that was in the vegetable. The rest will have been used by the animal for growth, producing heat, movement and waste.

3. **Energy used for any three of following:** Movement of animals; Respiration by animals; Maintaining body temperature of birds; Lost via animal waste

Waste Materials from Plants and Animals (pp 32–35)

1. Grass cuttings; Vegetable peelings; Teabags

2. algae; glucose; decomposers; decomposers
   (*1 correct = 1 mark; 2 correct = 2 marks; All 4 correct = 3 marks*)

3. **(a)** Jim
   (b) Jim's compost will be warm (black plastic) and will get oxygen because it is turned over; These are good conditions for bacteria to grow and digest the waste.
   (c) Any two from: If organic waste is sent to landfill, it will produce methane, which is a greenhouse gas; Recycling the waste means less space is taken up in landfill sites; People will not need to

buy peat-based compost (destruction of peat bogs is an environmental issue).
(d) The compost can be used on plants, avoiding the need to buy compost or fertilisers.

4. **(a)** Feeding D; Excretion A; Photosynthesis B; Respiration C
    (b) Combustion (burning)

5. **(a)** Tube D; Because it is warm and moist.
    (b) The soil/air/surface of the leaf
    (c) So that air could get in.
    (d) Accept one from: They could count the number of whole discs left at the end; They could record what fraction/percentage of leaf discs decayed and find an average. They could measure percentage decrease in mass of discs by measuring mass before and after time in soil.

Genetic Variation and its Control (pp 36–40)

1. **(a)** A – nucleus; B – cytoplasm; C – chromosomes; D – cell membrane.
    (b) fusion; DNA; variation

2. A; B; F

3. **(a)** B
    (b) E
    (c) B
    (d) I

4. **(a)** Enzymes
    (b) Any two from: They reproduce rapidly; They can be grown in large vats; They produce large quantities of insulin.

5. **(a)** characteristics; sexual; specialised; implanted; wombs
    (b) The original sheep may only have one or two young; By using embryo transplants, many new sheep can be produced in the same time period.
    (c) They all came from cells from the same embryo; So will have the same genes as each other; They will have a mixture of genes; Inherited from mother and father.
    (d) To treat diseases.

6. **(a) Any three from:** GM crops give higher yields; GM crops are insect resistant, reducing the use of pesticide; GM crops take up less land, leaving more for wildlife; GM crops can be enriched with nutrients, so are more healthy.
    (b) GM crops might breed with wild plants; GM crops may harm the insects that feed on them.
    (c) Any one from: To extend shelf life; Drought resistance

7. **(a)** 1 – A body cell is taken from a prize bull.
    2 – An unfertilised egg cell is taken from cow B.
    3 – The nucleus is removed from the egg cell.
    4 – The egg cell is fused with the body cell.
    5 – The fused cells start to divide to form an embryo.
    6 – The embryo is implanted into the womb of another cow.

(*All correct = 3 marks; 3 correct = 2 marks; 2 correct = 1 mark*)
(b) They are given an electric shock.

8. **(a)** one
    (b) gametes
    (c) the same as
    (d) clone

Evolution (pp 41–45)

1. **(a)** The giraffes would have been born with long neck or short neck genes; They could not grow long necks and change their genes during their lifetime.
    (b) Any two from: It was against their religion (God created the Earth); There was insufficient evidence at the time; People did not know about genes and mechanisms of inheritance.
    (c) five million

2. **(a)** 210 million years ago
    (b) Cretaceous
    (c) They have discovered fossils.
    (d) Lizard
    (e) Archosaur

3. All species in existence have developed from simple life forms over a period of approximately 3 billion years.

4. **This is a model answer that would score full marks**
    Darwin's theory is that there is much variation within species and that species compete for food, mates, etc. The individuals within the species that are the best suited/adapted will be more successful and will survive. They will therefore breed and pass on their genes to their offspring. This is known as 'survival of the fittest'. Those individuals that are not well adapted are less likely to survive and may become extinct.

5. **(a)** Some babies' skulls were found in their mothers' pouches.
    (b) It had giant claws.
    (c) The fossil finds suggest that they travelled in herds.
    (d) Extinct

6. **(a)** There are more striped snails in the countryside because the stripes camouflage them; In the forest, there are more plain snails where they blend in with the forest floor.
    (b) Brown; Because it is dark in the forest and the brown blends in with trees and forest floor.
    (c) Scotland
    (d) Less brown-shelled snails – brown shells may cause them to overheat; More yellow-shelled snails – no need to warm up the snail.

Cells and Simple Cell Transport (pp 46–50)

1.

Structure/ type of cell	Nucleus	Cytoplasm	Cell membrane	Cell wall
Plant cell	✓	✓	✓	✓
Bacterial cell	✗	✓	✓	✓
Animal cell	✓	✓	✓	✗

(*1 mark for each correct row*)

2. The cell has hair-like structures – To absorb water
The cell is very large – To act as a food supply
This cell has a tail – To swim
This cell can be very long with branched endings – To carry nerve impulses
(*1 correct = 1 mark; 2 correct = 2 marks; All 4 correct = 3 marks*)

3. **(a)** Red blood cell/Erythrocyte
(b) It leaves more room for haemoglobin/more room to carry oxygen.

4. **(a)** It contains chloroplasts.
(b) It does not have a cell wall.

5. **(a)** cytoplasm
(b) mitochondria
(c) ribosomes

6. **(a)** food; oxygen
(b) carbon dioxide; waste products

7. **(a)** 25mg/dl
(b) Between 0 and 120 minutes, the concentration of glucose inside the cell increases; Then it stops increasing.
(c) Glucose is moving; From the glucose solution into the cell; By diffusion.
(d) The concentration of glucose inside and outside the cell must be equal so there is no movement of glucose in either direction.

8. gases; high; low; faster.

9. **(a)** Leaf
(b) E; A; C; B; A; D; C; B

10. cytoplasm; cell wall; different substances; free within the cell

Tissues, Organs and Organ Systems (pp 51–53)

1. **(a)** A – salivary gland   B – stomach
C – liver   D – pancreas
E – small intestine   F – large intestine
(b) C
(c) Any one from: Enzymes; A named enzyme; Digestive juices.

2. Epidermal; mesophyll; gaps; gases

3. **(a) Any one from:** They work well; The patient's own blood vessels quickly grow into the graft.

(b) The new tissue will not get sufficient oxygen and glucose if blood supply is poor; The tissue will then die.
(c) Any one from: The new skin sometimes peels off when the artificial layer is removed; Artificial skin is not permanent.
(d) Artificial skin contains no living components, normal skin is made of living cells.
(e) Epithelial cells

4. Glandular – Can produce substances such as enzymes and hormones
Muscular – Can contract to bring about movement
Nervous – Can carry electrical impulses
Epithelial – A lining/covering tissue
(*1 correct = 1 mark; 2 correct = 2 marks; All 4 correct = 3 marks*)

5. **(a)** C
(b) A
(c) Any one from: Transport of nutrients; Transport of water (taken in by roots); Transport of sugar (made in the leaves).

Photosynthesis (pp 54–56)

1. water; oxygen

2. **(a) (i–ii) In any order:** Sunlight; Chlorophyll.
(b) (i) Chlorophyll
(ii) Inside the chloroplasts in a leaf cell.

3. Through their roots from the soil.

4. From the soil.

5. Amount of light; Amount of carbon dioxide; Temperature.

6. 45°C

7. The rate of photosynthesis increases with light intensity; So the less sunlight there is, the lower the rate of photosynthesis will be.

8. Amount of carbon dioxide or the temperature.

9. photosynthesis; grow

10. **(a)** To keep the water temperature constant.
(b) Keep all variables (except the one being investigated) the same, e.g. same amount of pondweed for each experiment, same amount of water for each experiment
(c) Repeat their investigation.

11. respiration in the plant

12. **Any two from:** Used to produce fat or oil for storage; Used to produce cellulose, which strengthens the cell wall; Used to produce proteins; Used to make starch used in respiration

13. **(a) Any one from:** Starch; Oils/Fats
(b) (i-ii) Roots; Leaves
(c) Respiration

14. **(a)** Light
(b) Accept one from: A negative result; No colour change.

(c) Repeat their investigation.

(d) A leaf that has not been covered up.

Organisms and their Environment (pp 57–58)

1. Availability of water; Availability of oxygen and carbon dioxide; Amount of light

2. **(a)** Place all the quadrats randomly in the field.
   (b) $(5 + 2 + 1 + 4 + 5 + 2 + 6 + 3) \div 10$;
   $= 28 \div 10 = 2.8$
   (c) 2.3×5400; $= 12\,420$

3. **(a)** *(1 mark for points correctly plotted; 1 mark for line drawn)*

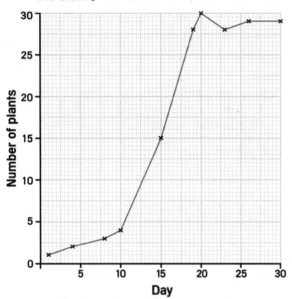

Day

   (b) The population is slowly increasing.
   (c) **Any two from:** Competition for space; Competition for water; Competition for light; Lack of nutrients and accumulation of waste products; Disease or deficiency

Proteins – their Functions and Uses (pp 59–62)

1. Amino acid molecules

2. **(a)** biological; speeds up
   (b) protein; amino acids

3. The enzyme's special shape will be destroyed; It will be unable to carry out its normal function.

4. **(a)** Liver
   (b) Gall bladder
   (c) Small intestine
   (d) It provides alkaline conditions in which enzymes in the small intestine work most effectively.

5. **(a–c) In any order:** Salivary glands; Pancreas; Small intestine.

6. Protease – Proteins – Amino acids; Amylase – Carbohydrates – Glucose; Lipase – Fats – Glycerol and fatty acids.

7. Salivary glands; Stomach; Pancreas; Small intestine

8. **(a)** Protease

(b) Amino acids
   (c) Type of enzyme
   (d) *(Correctly plotted bar chart – 1 mark for each bar)*

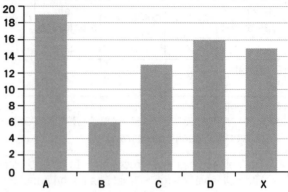

   (e) B; Because it is the quickest to completely pre-digest the protein.
   (f) Repeat the experiment several times.

9. Fat-digesting; Protein-digesting

10. A 3; B 2; C 1

11. **(a) (i–ii)** They work well at 25–45°C; They all work at atmospheric pressures.
    (b) (i–ii) Any two from: They are easily broken down by high temperature or the wrong pH; They are soluble in water, so it may be difficult to separate them from products; They are expensive.

12. **This is a model answer that would score full marks**
    As fructose is sweeter it can be used in smaller quantities, which makes it more cost-effective for the manufacturer. It also means that a person consuming the product will be taking in fewer calories, which will help in weight loss.

Aerobic and Anaerobic Respiration (pp 63–67)

1. **(a–c)** Muscle contraction; Metabolism; Maintaining temperature; Building larger molecules from smaller ones

2. Respiration in the presence of oxygen

3. During normal everyday activities.

4. oxygen; carbon dioxide

5. **(a)** contract
   (b) efficient

6. By the bloodstream.

7. In the mitochondria in the cytoplasm in cells

8. **(a–c) Any three from:** As sweat; In moist breath; In urine; In faeces

9. Respiration in the absence of oxygen

10. vigorous

11. Lactic acid

12. **(a)** True
    (b) True
    (c) False

13. **(a–c) Any three from:** Oxygen used in aerobic respiration; More energy from aerobic; Carbon dioxide and water end products of aerobic; Lactic acid end product of anaerobic.

14. increases; increase; increases; carbon dioxide; oxygen

15. glucose; increased; carbon dioxide

16. **(a)**

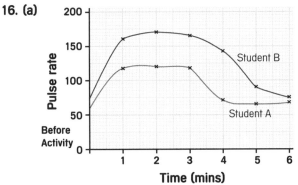

(*1 mark for points correctly plotted; 1 mark for line drawn; 1 mark for line labelled*)

(b) Student A

(c) (i–ii) Lower pulse rate increase; Quicker recovery time.

(d) Any two from: To get more oxygen to the muscles; To get more glucose to the muscles; Faster removal of carbon dioxide; Faster removal of lactic acid.

(e) Lactic acid

17. **(a)** Carbon dioxide
    (b) Turn cloudy
    (c) As a control
    (d) Carry out repeats using other beetles.
    (e) Any sensible answer, e.g. helps to develop knowledge; Beetle not harmed

18. **(a)** oxygen
    (b) fatigued/rubbery
    (c) oxygen debt

19. Aerobic respiration

20. **(a)** 30 minutes
    (b) 90 − 30 = 60 minutes
    (*1 for calculation, 1 for answer*)
    (c) It allows results to be fairly compared.
    (d) The second athlete
    (e) Oxygen

Cell Division and Inheritance (pp 68–74)

1. 46/23 pairs

2. Gametes

3. Half the number of chromosomes as a normal body cell

4. A zygote

5. **(a)** XX and XY
   (b) (i) female
       (ii) male

6. **(a)** Whether the ovum is fertilised by an X-carrying sperm or a Y-carrying sperm.

(b) 50%/half

7. **(a)** Gamete production
   (b) chromosome; genetic; parent
   (c) 2

8. **(a)** ovaries; eggs; chromosomes
   (b) Gametes

9. **(a)** 46
   (b) It divides repeatedly by mitosis to form a new individual.

10. **(a) (i–ii)** Human embryos; Adult bone marrow.
    (b) Stem cells can be made to differentiate into any type of cell; Including nerve cells and muscle cells.
    (c) (i–ii) Any two from: Expensive; High chance of rejection; Dependency on immunosuppressant drugs; Uncontrollable cell growth could cause cancer.

11. Two

12. dominant; recessive

13. Inheritance of genes.

14. **(a) (i)** Bb
        (ii) bb
    (b) 0%

15. **(a)** dominant
    (b) recessive

16. Double helix

17. **(a)** dominant; one
    (b) recessive; carriers

18. **(a)** Ff
    (b) ff

19. cells; structure; function

20. **(a)** BB = Homozygous dominant
    (b) Bb = Heterozygous
    (c) bb = Homozygous recessive

21. A 2; B 1; C 4; D 3

22. **(a)** Gametes: B; B; b; b (*1 mark*)
    Offspring: Bb; Bb; Bb; Bb (*1 mark*)
    (b) 100

23. By providing a code for a combination of amino acids that make up a protein.

24.

		White flower (rr)	
		Genotype of ovum (r)	Genotype of ovum (r)
Red flower (RR)	Genotype of pollen (R)	**(a)** Rr	**(b)** Rr
	Genotype of pollen (R)	**(c)** Rr	**(d)** Rr

25. **(a)** phenotype; genotype
    (b) homozygous
    (c) heterozygous
    (d) homozygous

26. Sex is controlled by sex chromosomes – XX in females, XY in males; There is a 50% chance of an offspring being a boy or girl; in order to produce females the sperm need to carry the X chromosome and not the Y chromosome.

27. (a) X
(b) X or Y
(c) Father's; Because the male chromosome can be X or Y, mother's egg can only give X chromosome.

28. (a) (i) short wing
(ii) nn
(b) Parents (female): nn (*1 mark*); Gametes (male): N, n; (female): n, n (*1 mark*); Offspring (male): Nn, nn; (female) Nn, nn (*1 mark*)
(c) 50%

Speciation (p 75)

1. Fossils

2. Any one from: From parts of organisms that have not decayed; When parts of the organism are replaced by other materials as they decay; As preserved traces of organisms, e.g. footprints; trapped in resin, e.g. amber

3. Any one from: Many early forms of life were soft-bodied, which means they left few traces behind; Many fossils are destroyed by geological activity; Many fossils are hidden in layers of rock that are not accessible; Most animals rot and do not fossilize

4. (a) When all individuals of a kind (species) have died.
(b) (i–iii) Any three from: New/increased competition; Change in environment; New predators; New disease; Single catastrophic event; Loss of habitat
(c) Accept named extinct animal, e.g. dodo, species of dinosaur

5. Isolation; Genetic variation; Natural selection; Speciation.

Movement of Molecules In and Out of Cells (pp 76–79)

1. carbon dioxide

2. (a) OM
(b) water; partially permeable; osmosis
(c) (No salt solution) like a control experiment to compare the other concentrations with salt against.

3. (a) along/down
(b) high; low

4. (a–b) Active transport moves substances against (or up) a concentration gradient; Requires energy

5. (a–b) Any two suitable answers, e.g. Ions; Sugar

6. specialised/adapted; exchange/transport

7. (a) (i–ii) Any two from: Large surface area; Large network of blood vessels; Thin membrane.
(b) (i) Microvilli create an even larger surface area; So more digested food can be absorbed/can be absorbed faster.
(ii) Mitochondria provide energy; Necessary for the uptake of digested nutrients by active transport.
(c) There will be less absorption of digested food.

8. Ribs 3; Bronchus 1; Diaphragm 4; Windpipe 2; Alveoli 5

9. trachea; cartilage

10. (a) Carbon dioxide
(b) Oxygen

11. Good blood supply; Large surface area

12. Carbon dioxide

13. (a) Healthy man
(b) Less oxygen absorbed into the blood; So less respiration carried out to release energy
(c) Smoking

Transport Systems in Plants and Animals (pp 80–84)

1. To transport substances around the body

2. (a) Any three from: Heart; Blood vessels (arteries, veins and capillaries); Blood (white blood cells, red blood cells, plasma and platelets)
(b) In any order: glucose/oxygen; carbon dioxide

3. (a) Oxygenated blood
(b) Deoxygenated blood

4. (a) Lungs; oxygen
(b) twice

5. (a) Artery
(b) Vein

6. (i–ii) Gains oxygen; Loses carbon dioxide

7. thin; absorbed or transported; narrow

8. Artery 3; Vein 1; Capillaries in the body 4; Capillaries in the lungs 2.

9. (a–d) Plasma; Platelets; Red blood cells; White blood cells

10. cells or organs; lungs; glucose; liver; kidneys

11. oxygen; haemoglobin; oxyhaemoglobin

12. (a) an atrium
(b) an artery
(c) a valve

13. (a) xylem
(b) phloem

14. They provide a large surface area; through which water and dissolved minerals/ions are absorbed.

15. (a) large
(b) Any two from: Broad; Thin; Flat

16. Transpiration

17. (a) 12:00
(b) It is the hottest time of the day when water evaporates most quickly.

18. (a–c) Hot; Dry; Windy

19. X = guard cell; Y = stoma

20. (a) (i) Cool, damp, in the light and not very windy.
  (ii) Transpiration and diffusion of gases occurs.
 (b) (i) Hot, dry and windy.
  (ii) To prevent transpiration and diffusion of gases.
  (iii) Photosynthesis.

21. (a) (i) X
  (ii) It has no stomata on the upper surface or has the lowest number of stomata on upper surface; So less transpiration/evaporation or water loss.
 (b) It reduces water loss, having less on upper surface; Lower surface tends to be in shade.

Homeostasis (pp 85–89)

1. **(a–e)** Water content; Temperature; Ion content; Blood sugar; Urea

2. (a) respiration
 (b) lungs
 (c) liver
 (d) amino acids

3. (a–c) They regulate the amount of water in your blood; They regulate the amount of ions in your blood; They remove all urea.

4. The body can't remove excess substances if the kidneys fail. This will ultimately result in death.

5. (a–c) Dissolved ions; Water, Urea

6. (a) Liver
 (b) Kidney
 (c) Amino acids

7. Useful substances return to the blood.

8. water/ion; ion/water; osmosis.

9. (a) partially permeable
 (b) blood; glucose; mineral

10. To remove wastes that build up in the body

11. False

12. (a) The body could reject the kidney.
 (b) The immune system, which may fight the donated kidney as it sees it as a 'foreign object'.
 (c) (i–ii) Any two from: The recipient is kept in sterile conditions; Drugs are given to suppress the immune system; Donor kidney must have a tissue type similar to that of the recipient.

13. Protein molecules are too large to be filtered from the blood in the kidneys.

14. reabsorbed

15. Bladder

16. decreases

17. Liver

18. The pancreas does not produce insulin.

19. By controlling their diet

20. Any one from: Insulin; Glucagon

21. (a) Brain
 (b) 37°C

22. (a) less
 (b) more

23. (a) (i–iii) Muscles contract and relax quickly causing shivering; Sweat glands in the skin stop releasing sweat; Blood vessels supplying the skin capillaries constrict leaving a pale colour to the skin.
 (b) (i–ii) Blood vessels supplying the skin capillaries dilate; Sweat glands release sweat.

24. (a) Glycogen
 (b) Liver
 (c) Glucagon
 (d) Pancreas
 (e) When blood glucose levels fall too low.

25. (a–b) Blood vessels supplying skin capillaries constrict; Muscles start to shiver.

26. (a) (i) increase
  (ii) decrease
 (b) When it is hot we produce less urine because we are sweating more; which helps to cool us down.

Humans and their Environment (pp 90–98)

1. **Any sensible answers, including any two from:** Pollution; Dumping waste; Using up raw materials; Deforestation; Building houses; Global warming; Quarrying

2. (a) This is a model answer that would score full marks
 Exponentially means with increasing speed, so in this case it means that the birth rate is greater than the death rate. The human population might be increasing in this way due to better standards of living and better health care.
 (b) (i) With sewage, fertilisers or toxic chemicals.
  (ii) With smoke and gases, such as carbon dioxide, sulfur dioxide and oxides of nitrogen, which contribute to acid rain.
  (iii) With toxic chemicals such as pesticides and herbicides, which may be washed from land into water.

3. Carbon dioxide; Methane; Sulfur dioxide

4. Cause acid rain; Kill trees and plants; Increase carbon dioxide.

5. **Accept any suitable answer,** e.g. Lichens; Freshwater shrimp; Mayfly nymph

6. (a) fertilisers
 (b) pesticides
 (c) herbicides

7. **Accept one from:** Moral reasons; May be of use to humans in the future.

8. (a) Cutting down large areas of forest
 (b) Increase in the amount of carbon dioxide in the air.

9. **(a–b) Any two from:** To provide land for agricultural use; To build roads; To build mines; To build buildings

10. Carbon dioxide

11. Photosynthesis

12. **(a)** tropical; trees; carbon dioxide; biodiversity; extinct; habitats.

13. The nutrients in the soil are absorbed by the crops and are not replaced.

14. gases; heat; warming

15. **(a–b)** Methane; Carbon dioxide.

16. Deforestation: Burning fossil fuels; A growth in cattle farming; Growing rice

17. Climate change: A rise in sea levels

18. **(a)** The presence of water or metabisulfate.
    (b) To keep the gases in.
    (c) (i) That sodium metabisulfate affects (decreases) the germination of cress seeds.
    (ii) No; They need to carry out repeats to increase the reliability of their results.
    (iii) Any two from: Amount of light; Temperature; Competition for space.

19. Increasing the amount of metal recycled – Fewer quarries are dug to provide raw materials; Using fewer pesticides and fertilisers – Less pollution of rivers flowing through farmland; Reducing sulfur dioxide emissions – Less acid rain is produced; Increasing the amount of paper recycled – Fewer forests are cut down.

20. **(a)** The range of species in a habitat.
    (b) Any one from: They may have future uses or moral duty; To maintain food webs and interactions between organisms in an environment.

21. **(a) (i)** methane
    (ii) waste; carbohydrate
    (iii) temperature
    (b) (i) (26 000 + 3000 + 7000) – 11 000
       = 36 000 – 11 000 = 25 000
       (*1 for calculation, 1 for correct answer*)
    (ii) $\frac{250\ 000}{25\ 000}$ = 10 years

22. Anaerobic fermentation

23. Produces food for consumption now; but conserves resources so that food can continue to be produced in the same way by future generations.

24. **(a)** Introduce quotas
    (b) Increase mesh size.

25. **(a)** A fungus
    (b) Glucose syrup

26. **Accept one from:** There is a greater carbon dioxide output (from respiration) from sheep since it takes longer to produce sheep meat; Sheep require more space, therefore more land is taken up to rear sheep. This land may otherwise have been forest.

27. **(a)** 100 kJ – (6 kJ + 61 kJ)
       100 kJ – 67 kJ = 33 kJ
       (*1 for calculation, 1 for correct answer*)
    (b) 61 kJ + 33 kJ = 94 kJ
       (*1 for calculation, 1 for correct answer*)
    (c) Limit the movement of animals; Heat their surroundings

28. **(a)** Housing animals close together in indoor pens.
    (b) (i–iii) Any three from: Accommodation can be cheap and easy to secure from predators; Environmental conditions (light and temperature) can be controlled; Energy isn't wasted on movement or generating heat by the animal so it is a more energy-efficient transfer; Produces a cheap product for the farmer to sell easily in a competitive market.
    (c) (i–iii) Any three from: Disease can spread very quickly in crowded areas, which sometimes means expensive antibiotics for the farmer to purchase; Cramped conditions can cause negative behaviour in the animals, who may fight and injure or kill other animals; Animal welfare standards may not be met; Environmental conditions are controlled by using equipment that relies on burning fossil fuels.

29. **(a)** Because customers are concerned with environmental issues.
    (b) Helps to reduce food miles; So fewer greenhouse gases are released from transport.

30. The destruction of peat bogs and other areas of peat releases carbon dioxide into the atmosphere; Reduces habitat destruction/loss

1. The diagram below shows the human digestive system

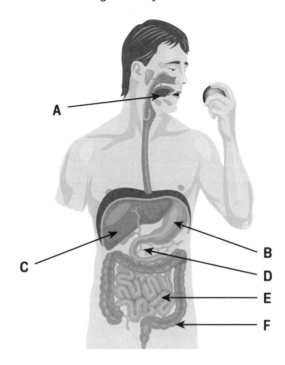

A

C

B

D

E

F

(a) Name the parts labelled A to F. (6 marks)

A .... B ....

C .... D ....

E .... F ....

(b) Write the letter of the organ that produces bile. (1 mark)

....

(c) The pancreas is a gland and produces the hormone insulin. Name **one** other substance produced by the pancreas. (1 mark)

....

2. Complete the following passage by filling in the blanks, using some of the words below. (4 marks)

gaps   epidermal   chloroplasts   phloem

water   mesophyll   gases

Plants, like animals, have different tissues. .... tissue is found covering the

outer layers of the leaf. The .... tissue carries out photosynthesis. The cells

of this tissue have .... between them to allow easy passage

of ....

3. Read the following passage about burns and skin grafts.

> Patients with severe burns often require skin grafts. There are three options available.
>
> If the burn is not too severe, the burnt skin is removed and a thin layer of skin taken from an unburnt area of the patient is grafted on. Usually these grafts work well and the patient's own blood vessels quickly grow into the graft.
>
> If the patient has lost most of their skin through burns, scientists have developed a way of taking just a small piece of skin from the patient and growing this in the laboratory to form a layer of skin for grafting. The problem with these tissue-engineered sheets of skin is that growth of new blood vessels is slow, often leading to loss of the grafts.
>
> Another alternative for serious burns is artificial skin, which contains no living components. It is composed of silicon and collagen. This is not intended as a replacement skin, but is draped over the burn area and stimulates new skin to grow underneath it. Sometimes the new layer of skin is peeled off when the artificial layer is removed.

(a) Suggest **one** advantage of normal skin grafts. (1 mark)

....

(b) Why should slow growth of blood vessels in tissue-engineered sheets of skin lead to loss of grafts? (2 marks)

....

....

(c) Suggest **one** disadvantage of artificial skin grafts. (1 mark)

....

(d) What is the main difference between artificial skin and normal skin? (1 mark)

....

(e) The diagram shows part of a tissue-engineered sheet of skin cells.

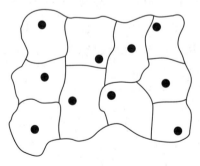

What is the name of these cells? (1 mark)

....

4. Organs are made up of a number of tissues. Match the type of tissue in **List A** with its function in **List B**. Draw a line to match each type with its function. (3 marks)

List A

| Glandular |

| Muscular |

| Nervous |

| Epithelial |

List B

| Can contract to bring about movement |

| A lining/covering tissue |

| Can carry electrical impulses |

| Can produce substances such as enzymes and hormones |

5. The picture below shows a plant.

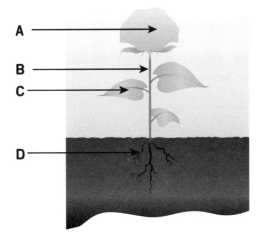

(a) Write the letter of the plant organ that is responsible for photosynthesis. (1 mark)

_____

(b) Write the letter of the plant organ that is responsible for reproduction. (1 mark)

_____

(c) What is the function of organ B? (1 mark)

_____

(Total: _____ **/ 24 marks)**

B2 Photosynthesis

1. Complete the following equation for photosynthesis. (2 marks)

   carbon dioxide + ... ⟶ glucose + ...

2. (a) Apart from the ingredients given in the equation above, what **two** other factors are required for photosynthesis? (2 marks)

   (i) ....

   (ii) ....

   (b) (i) What is the name of the green pigment that absorbs the Sun's energy during photosynthesis? (1 mark)

   ....

   (ii) Where is this pigment found in the cell? (1 mark)

   ....

3. Where do plants obtain water required for photosynthesis? (1 mark)

   ....

4. Plants need nitrates to produce proteins. Where do plants obtain nitrates from?
   Tick the box next to the correct answer. (1 mark)

   From the soil ☐

   From the leaves ☐

   From oxygen ☐

   From photosynthesis ☐

5. Which of the following are factors that can limit the rate of photosynthesis?
   Tick the boxes next to the **three** correct options. (3 marks)

   Amount of oxygen ☐

   Amount of light ☐

   Amount of carbon dioxide ☐

   Amount of chlorophyll ☐

   Temperature ☐

6. Circle the correct temperature option in the following sentence. (1 mark)

   The temperature at which enzymes controlling photosynthesis are destroyed is

   14°C / 25°C / 32°C / 45°C

7. Explain why too little light can have a negative effect on a plant. (2 marks)

....

....

8. A plant is receiving plenty of light but its rate of photosynthesis stops increasing. What other factors might be responsible? Tick the box next to the correct option. (1 mark)

Amount of carbon dioxide or the amount of oxygen ◯

Amount of carbon dioxide or the temperature ◯

Amount of chlorophyll or the temperature ◯

Amount of glucose or the amount of oxygen ◯

9. Fill in the missing words to complete the following sentence. (2 marks)

To control the rate of .... greenhouses can be used to make plants

.... more quickly, becoming bigger and stronger.

10. Some students investigated the effect of temperature on the rate of photosynthesis in pondweed. They set up the equipment shown below and changed the temperature using ice and hot water. They counted the number of bubbles given off every minute at different temperatures.

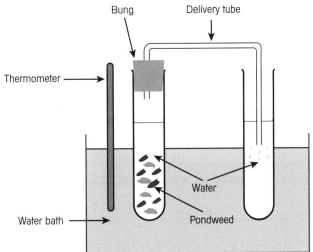

Bung   Delivery tube

Thermometer

Water

Water bath   Pondweed

(a) Why did the students use a water bath? (1 mark)

....

(b) What should the students have done to make the investigation fair? (1 mark)

....

(c) How could the students make sure their results were reliable? (1 mark)

....

11. Most of the carbon dioxide that a plant uses during photosynthesis is absorbed from the air.

Give **one** other source of carbon dioxide for a plant. Draw a circle around your answer. (1 mark)

the soil   respiration in the plant   osmosis in the plant   water

12. Describe **two** uses of glucose in plants and algae. (2 marks)

....

....

13. Glucose is difficult for plants to store.

(a) What is glucose changed into? (1 mark)

....

(b) Apart from stems, give **two** other places where plants store this substance. (2 marks)

(i) ....

(ii) ....

(c) State the reaction that uses glucose in plants. (1 mark)

....

14. A group of students carried out a common experiment to prove that leaves carry out photosynthesis. They selected one plant from their classroom window and covered part of a single leaf in foil. The students then carried out experiments testing for the presence of starch using iodine, a yellowy brown liquid. A positive test will turn iodine blue/black.

(a) What is prevented from reaching the leaf by the foil? (1 mark)

....

(b) If the leaf covered in foil was tested for starch using iodine, what result would you expect? (1 mark)

....

(c) One student suggests that they should make their results more reliable. What should they do? (1 mark)

....

(d) Another student in the class says that they should have a control in their investigation. What would they use as the control? (1 mark)

....

(Total: .... / 31 marks)

1. Temperature and availability of nutrients are two physical factors that affect the distribution of organisms. What other factors affect the distribution of organisms? Tick **three** options. (3 marks)

Amount of carbon monoxide ◯   Availability of water ◯

Availability of oxygen and carbon dioxide ◯   Amount of light ◯

Availability of lichens ◯   Availability of rocks ◯

2. A class of students was asked to estimate the number of daisies on the school field. The field is 60m by 90m and has an area of $5400m^2$. They decided to use quadrats that were $1m^2$.

   (a) Which is the best way of using quadrats in this investigation? Tick **one** option. (1 mark)

   Place all the quadrats where there are lots of plants. ◯

   Place all the quadrats randomly in the field. ◯

   Place all the quadrats where dandelions do not grow. ◯

   Each student collected data by using ten quadrats. The results of one student, Shaun, are shown in the table below.

Quadrat	1	2	3	4	5	6	7	8	9	10
Number of daisies	5	2	1	0	4	5	2	0	6	3

   (b) Calculate the mean number of dandelions per quadrat counted by Shaun. Show clearly how you worked out your answer. (2 marks)

   ....

   ....

   (c) Another student, Bethany, calculated a mean of 2.3 daisies per quadrat from her results. Using Bethany's results, estimate the total number of daisies in the whole field by using the equation below. Show clearly how you work out your answer. (2 marks)

   Estimated number of daisies on the field = Mean number of daisies per quadrat × Number of quadrats that would fit in the field

   ....

   ....

   Estimated number of daisies on the field ....

3. Duckweed is a small floating plant found in ponds. It reproduces quite quickly to produce large populations. Helen decided to investigate duckweed by growing some in a beaker of water. She counted the number of duckweed at regular intervals. Her results are shown in the table below.

Day	1	4	8	10	15	19	20	23	26	30
Number of plants	1	2	3	4	15	28	30	28	29	29

(a) Plot a graph of the results to show how the population changed over time. (2 marks)

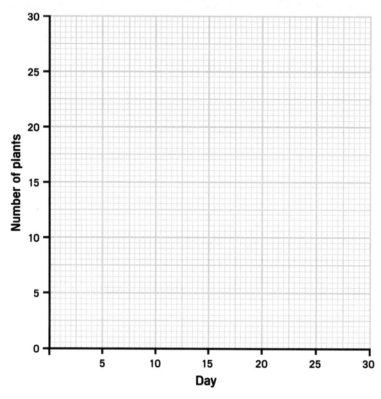

(b) Describe what is happening to the population between day one and day ten. (1 mark)

....

(c) Suggest **two** factors that could have prevented the population from continuing to increase. (2 marks)

....

....

(Total: .... **/ 13 marks)**

1. What are protein molecules made up of? Tick **one** option. (1 mark)

    Glucose molecules ☐

    Starch molecules ☐

    Amino acid molecules ☐

    Glycerol and fatty acid molecules ☐

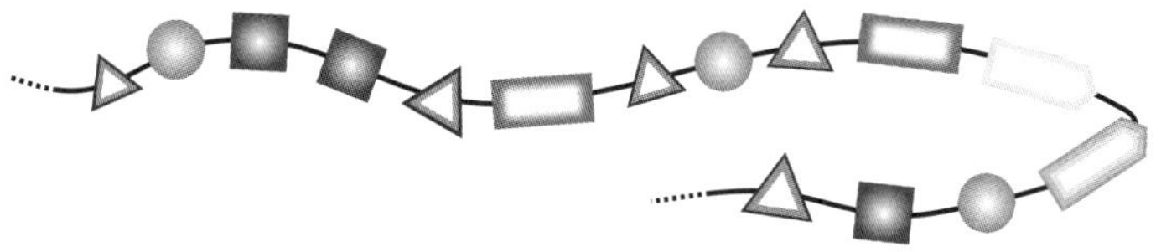

2. Circle the correct options in the following sentences.

    (a) An enzyme is a **biological / chemical** catalyst that **speeds up / slows down** the rate of reactions in an organism. (2 marks)

    (b) Enzymes are made from **carbohydrate / fat / vitamin / protein** molecules. They are made up of long chains of **DNA / amino acids / fatty acids / starch** molecules. (2 marks)

3. Briefly explain what happens to an enzyme if the temperature goes too high. (2 marks)

4. **(a)** Name the organ in the body that produces bile. (1 mark)

    (b) Where is bile stored in the human body? (1 mark)

    (c) Into which part of the digestive system is bile released? (1 mark)

    (d) Why is it necessary for bile to neutralise the acid that was added to food in the stomach? (1 mark)

5. Amylase is a carbohydrase enzyme. List **three** places in the digestive system where it is produced. (3 marks)

    (a)

    (b)

    (c)

6. Different enzymes act on specific nutrients. Draw lines to match the correct enzyme to the nutrient it works on, then match the correct nutrient with its smaller sub-unit. (3 marks)

Protease
Amylase
Lipase

Fats
Proteins
Carbohydrates

Amino acids
Glycerol and fatty acids
Glucose

7. Which of the following organs produce digestive enzymes? Tick **four** correct options. (4 marks)

Rectum ◻

Large intestine ◻

Salivary glands ◻

Stomach ◻

Gall bladder ◻

Pancreas ◻

Small intestine ◻

Liver ◻

8. Enzymes are used in industry and in the home. Enzymes are often used in the manufacture of baby food to help pre-digest certain foods.

(a) When proteins are pre-digested in industry, what type of enzyme is used? (1 mark)

_____

(b) What will these enzymes produce? (1 mark)

_____

A baby food manufacturer wants to improve the efficiency of his business and use the enzyme that pre-digests the protein the fastest. He already uses enzyme X, which takes 15 minutes to completely pre-digest the protein.

He investigates four other enzymes; A, B, C and D. He uses the same concentration of enzyme as well as the same amount of protein for each experiment. The table below shows the time taken for the enzymes 'investigated' to completely pre-digest the protein.

Enzyme	A	B	C	D
Time taken to completely pre-digest protein (minutes)	19	6	13	16

(c) What is the independent variable being tested? (1 mark)

(d) The manufacturer started plotting the results on the chart below. Complete the chart by plotting the remaining results. (4 marks)

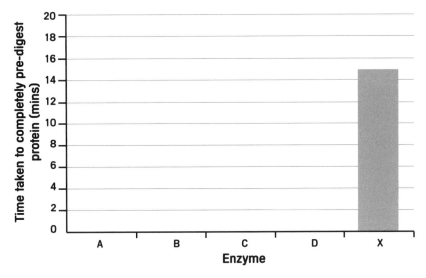

(e) Which enzyme would you recommend the manufacturer should use? Explain why. (2 marks)

(f) The research and development team at the company are not convinced by the results from this investigation. What could the manufacturer do to increase the reliability of their results? (1 mark)

9. Which **two** enzymes might biological detergents contain? Tick the **two** correct options. (2 marks)

Fat-digesting ⬭

Glucose-digesting ⬭

Bile-digesting ⬭

Protein-digesting ⬭

10. Match statements **A**, **B**, and **C** with the enzymes **1–3** listed below. Write the appropriate numbers in the boxes provided. (3 marks)

    1. Carbohydrases   **2. Proteases**   **3. Isomerases**

A Used to produce fructose syrup used in slimming foods ⬭

B Used to pre-digest protein in baby foods ⬭

C Used to convert starch into sugar syrup ⬭

11. Here are some of the properties of enzymes:

- They are easily broken down by high temperature or the wrong pH.

- They are soluble in water, so it may be difficult to separate them from products.

- They are expensive.

- They work well at 25–45°C.

- They all work at atmospheric pressures.

Use only the information above to answer the following questions.

(a) Give **two** advantages of using enzymes in industry. (2 marks)

(i) ....

(ii) ....

(b) Give **two** disadvantages of using enzymes in industry. (2 marks)

(i) ....

(ii) ....

12. *In this question you will be assessed on using good English, organising information and using specialist terms where appropriate.*

Fructose syrup is much sweeter than glucose syrup. Explain why manufacturers of slimming foods use fructose syrup rather than glucose syrup. (4 marks)

....

....

....

....

(Total: .... **/ 44 marks)**

1. List **three** things that the energy produced in aerobic respiration is used for. (3 marks)

    (a) ....

    (b) ....

    (c) ....

2. What is aerobic respiration? Tick the correct option. (1 mark)

    Respiration in the absence of oxygen ◯

    Respiration in the presence of oxygen ◯

    Respiration that produces lactic acid ◯

    Respiration that uses carbon dioxide ◯

3. Describe when aerobic respiration occurs. (1 mark)

    ....

4. Fill in the missing gaps to complete the word equation for aerobic respiration. (1 mark)

    glucose + ... ⟶ .... + water + energy

5. Fill in the missing words to complete the following sentences. (2 marks)

    (a) Energy from respiration is used to enable muscles to ....

    (b) Aerobic respiration is a very .... way of producing energy.

6. How do glucose and oxygen get to the respiring cells? (1 mark)

    ....

7. Name where most of the reactions involved in aerobic respiration take place. (1 mark)

    ....

8. List **three** ways in which the water produced in aerobic respiration is lost from the body. (3 marks)

    (a) ....

    (b) ....

    (c) ....

9. What is anaerobic respiration? Tick the correct option. (1 mark)

Respiration in the absence of oxygen ☐

Respiration in the presence of oxygen ☐

Respiration that uses lactic acid ☐

Respiration that uses carbon dioxide ☐

10. Circle the correct option in the following sentence. (1 mark)

If our muscles are subjected to long periods of **light / vigorous / slow** activity, they become fatigued.

11. What is the waste product of anaerobic respiration? Tick the correct option. (1 mark)

Hydrochloric acid ☐

Sulfuric acid ☐

Lactic acid ☐

Aerobic respiration ☐

12. Are these sentences **true** or **false**? Circle the correct option. (3 marks)

(a) Lactic acid makes the muscles feel tired and rubbery. True / False

(b) Anaerobic respiration produces a small amount of energy quickly. True / False

(c) Anaerobic respiration is more efficient than aerobic respiration. True / False

13. List **three** differences between aerobic and anaerobic respiration. (3 marks)

(a) ....

(b) ....

(c) ....

14. Circle the correct options in the following paragraph. (5 marks)

When you exercise your heart rate **decreases / increases**, which causes the flow of blood to your muscles to **decrease / increase**. When you exercise your breathing rate also **increases / decreases** to speed up the removal of **carbon dioxide / oxygen** from your muscles and the transport of **carbon dioxide / oxygen** to your muscles.

15. Fill in the missing words to complete the following sentences. (3 marks)

During exercise, the supply of oxygen and .... is ....

This speeds up the removal of ....

16. Two students wanted to find out who was the fittest. They carried out a simple investigation where they did star jumps for three minutes. They recorded their pulse rate before the activity and every minute afterwards. Their results are given in the table below.

Time (mins)	Pulse rate (beats/min)	
	Student A	**Student B**
Before activity	68	72
1 minute after	116	160
2 minutes after	120	175
3 minutes after	116	168
4 minutes after	72	148
5 minutes after	66	92
6 minutes after	68	76

The results for student A have been plotted on the graph below.

(a) Add the data from Student B's column to the graph (1 mark)

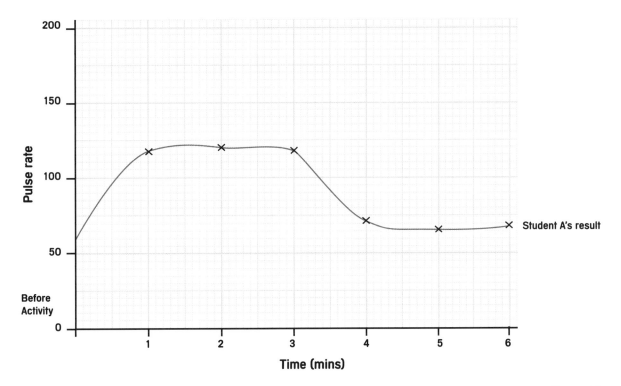

(b) Suggest which student was fitter. Draw a ring around your answer. (1 mark)

Student A / Student B

(c) Give **two** reasons for your answer. (2 marks)

(i) ....

(ii) ....

(d) Explain why the pulse rate in both students increased. Give **two** reasons.　　　　(2 marks)

_____

_____

(e) Both students experienced fatigue in their muscles. What substance caused the fatigue?　　(1 mark)

_____

17. Shaun wanted to prove that beetles carried out respiration. He filled two boiling tubes, A and B, with $2cm^3$ of limewater. In boiling tube A he rested a live beetle on a piece of gauze halfway up the tube (the beetle was not touching the limewater). Tube B contained only limewater. Both boiling tubes were sealed with a bung.

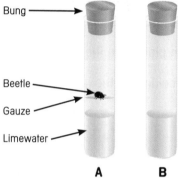

Bung

Beetle

Gauze

Limewater

A　　**B**

(a) What gas is limewater used to test for?　　　　(1 mark)

_____

(b) What would you expect to happen to the limewater in tube A?　　　　(1 mark)

_____

(c) Why did Shaun set up tube B?　　　　(1 mark)

_____

(d) How could Shaun increase the reliability of his results?　　　　(1 mark)

_____

(e) Shaun's friend said that he was cruel to use live animals in an experiment. Is Shaun right to carry out such experiments? Explain your answer.　　　　(1 mark)

_____

(Total: _____ / 44 marks)

18. Fill in the missing words to complete the following sentences. (3 marks)

(a) Anaerobic respiration occurs when the lungs and bloodstream cannot deliver enough

.... to the cells.

(b) When lactic acid builds up in the tissues, the muscles become ....

(c) The amount of oxygen needed to break down the lactic acid in tissues is called

the ....

19. Is more energy produced during aerobic respiration or anaerobic respiration? (1 mark)

....

20. A sports scientist investigated the amount of lactic acid produced in the leg muscle of a short-distance runner. His results are given in the table below.

Time (minutes)	0	10	20	30	40	50	60	70	80	90
Lactic acid (arbitrary units)	0	1	6	13	8	6	4	3	1	0

(a) When did the level of lactic acid reach a maximum? (1 mark)

....

(b) How long does it take for the lactic acid to be removed from the muscle? (2 marks)

....

(c) The lactic acid of a second athlete is investigated in the same way. Why is it important to keep variables the same in an investigation? (1 mark)

....

(d) It takes 20 minutes for the level of lactic acid in the second athlete's muscles to return to normal. Which athlete is the fittest? (1 mark)

....

(e) What gas is needed to break down the lactic acid? (1 mark)

....

(Total: .... **/ 10 marks)**

1. How many chromosomes does a human body cell contain? (1 mark)

2. What are the sex cells known as? Tick the correct option. (1 mark)

    Genes ⬜

    Alleles ⬜

    Gametes ⬜

    Chromosomes ⬜

3. What do the sex cells contain? Tick the correct option. (1 mark)

    Half the number of chromosomes as a normal body cell ⬜

    The same number of chromosomes as a normal body cell ⬜

    Twice the number of chromosomes as a normal body cell ⬜

    Half the number of chromosomes of a sperm cell ⬜

4. What is produced from the fusion of two sex cells? (1 mark)

5. **(a)** Circle the correct pair of sex chromosomes from the following options. (1 mark)

    XY and YY   **XX and XY**   **XX and YY**   **XF and XM**

    (b) Which of the following are the female sex chromosomes, and which are the male sex chromosomes. Label them correctly. (1 mark)

    (i) _____   **(ii)** _____

6. **(a)** Explain what determines the sex of an individual. (1 mark)

    (b) What is the likelihood of having a baby boy? (1 mark)

7. Mitosis is the division of body cells to make new cells.

(a) When is mitosis not used in dividing cells? Tick the correct option. (1 mark)

Asexual reproduction ☐   Gamete production ☐

Repair ☐   Growth ☐

(b) Fill in the missing words to complete the following sentences. (3 marks)

A copy of each _____ is made before a cell divides. The new cell has the

same _____ information as the _____ cell.

(c) Circle the correct option in the following sentence. (1 mark)

When one cell has undergone mitosis **1 / 2 / 4 / 8** 'daughter' cells will be made.

8. **(a)** Fill in the missing words to complete the following sentence. (3 marks)

Meiosis takes place in the _____ and testes, and produces

_____ and sperm containing 23 _____ .

(b) What type of cells are produced in meiosis? (1 mark)

_____

9. During human fertilisation the male and female sex cells join.

(a) How many chromosomes will the resulting cell contain? (1 mark)

_____

(b) Describe what happens to the new cell. (1 mark)

_____

10. **(a)** In which **two** places would you find stem cells? (2 marks)

(i) _____

(ii) _____

(b) Explain why stem cells can be used to treat conditions such as paralysis. (2 marks)

_____

_____

(c) Give **two** disadvantages of using stem cells. (2 marks)

(i) _____

(ii) _____

B2 Cell Division and Inheritance

11. How many alleles does the gene controlling tongue-rolling ability have? Tick the correct option. (1 mark)

One ☐

Two ☐

Three ☐

Four ☐

12. Fill in the missing words to complete the following sentences. (2 marks)

Where there are different alleles for a gene, the more powerful one is known as the

_____ allele and the weaker one is known as the _____ allele.

13. What does a genetic cross diagram show? (1 mark)

_____

14. (a) John has blue eyes. Both his parents have brown eyes. His mother's alleles are Bb.

(i) What must John's father's alleles be? Tick the correct option. (1 mark)

Bb ☐

BB ☐

bb ☐

BBb ☐

(ii) What alleles does John have? _____ (1 mark)

(b) Circle the correct option in the following sentence. (1 mark)

If both parents have blue eyes there is a **0% / 24% / 50% / 100%** chance that they will have a child with brown eyes.

15. Fill in the missing words to complete the following sentences.

(a) A _____ allele will control the characteristics of a gene if it is present on only one chromosome, or if it is present on both chromosomes. (1 mark)

(b) A _____ allele will only control the characteristic of a gene if it is present on both chromosomes. (1 mark)

16. What do the two strands of a DNA molecule coil together to form? Tick the correct box. (1 mark)

Double spring ☐   Double spiral ☐

Double twist ☐   Double helix ☐

17. Fill in the missing words to complete the following sentences. (4 marks)

(a) Polydactyly is a disorder that causes extra fingers or toes. It's caused by a _____

allele. Only _____ parent needs to have the disorder.

(b) Cystic fibrosis is caused by a _____ allele. It must be inherited from both

parents. The parents might not have the disorder, but they might be _____ .

18. The diagram below shows the inheritance of cystic fibrosis in a family.

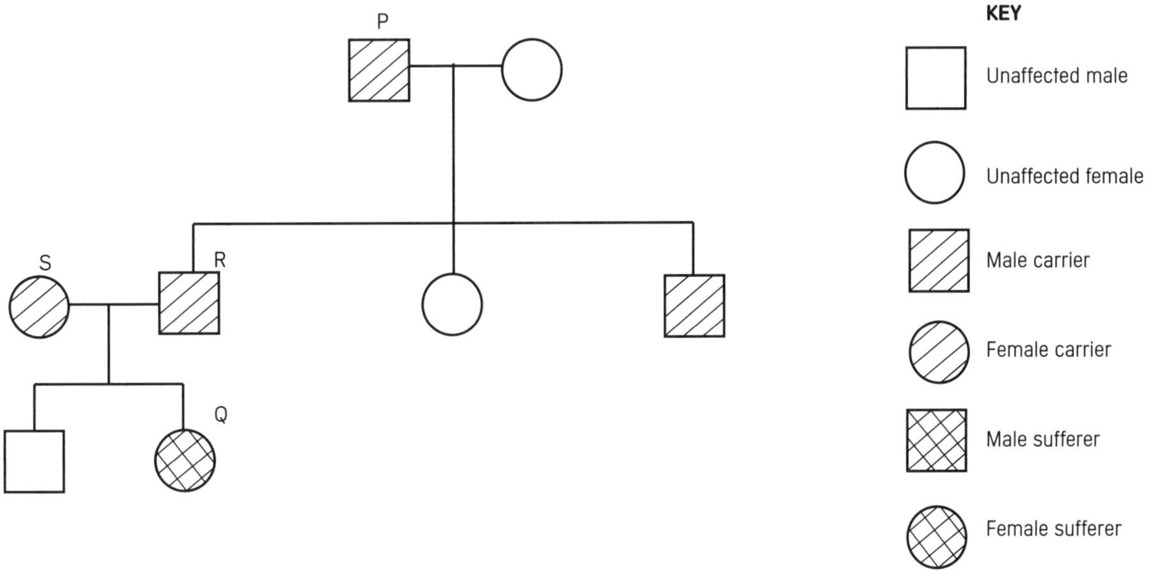

KEY

☐ Unaffected male

◯ Unaffected female

▨ Male carrier

⊘ Female carrier

▨ Male sufferer

⊗ Female sufferer

Cystic fibrosis is caused by a recessive allele, f. The dominant allele of the gene is represented by F.

(a) Give the alleles for person P _____ . (1 mark)

(b) Give the alleles for person Q _____ (1 mark)

19. Choose the correct words from the options given to complete the following sentence. (3 marks)

structure   function   cells

Differentiation is the result of _____ developing a specialised

_____ to carry out a specific _____ .

(Total: _____ / 44 marks)

B2 | Cell Division and Inheritance

20. Using the correct genetic terms, describe the following alleles. (3 marks)

(a) BB ....

(b) Bb ....

(c) bb ....

21. Match definitions **A**, **B**, **C** and **D** with the keywords **1–4** listed below. Write the appropriate numbers in the boxes provided. (4 marks)

1. Dominant	**2. Phenotype**
3. Heterozygous	**4. Homozygous**

A What the organism looks like ☐   **B** The stronger allele ☐

C Both alleles are the same ☐   **D** Different alleles ☐

22. (a) Complete this genetic diagram to show the possible genotypes of the offspring. (2 marks)

Brown eyes   x   Blue eyes

Parents   BB   X   bb

Gametes ◯ ◯   ◯ ◯

Offspring ◯ ◯ ◯ ◯

(b) Complete the following sentence. (1 mark)

There is a .... % chance that the offspring will have brown eyes.

23. How do genes code for a particular characteristic? (1 mark)

....

....

24. Rita likes to grow plants. One particular plant she grows can either have red flowers (homozygous dominant) or white flowers (homozygous recessive). She decides to cross the pollen from the red plant with ovum from the white.

Complete the genetic cross diagram below using R to represent the dominant allele and r for the recessive allele. (4 marks)

White flower (rr)

		Genotype of ovum (r)	Genotype of ovum (r)
Red flower (RR)	Genotype of pollen (R)	**(a)**	**(b)**
	Genotype of pollen (R)	**(c)**	**(d)**

25. Complete the following sentences by circling the correct words in bold. (5 marks)

(a) A pea plant with a tall **genotype / phenotype** could have a **genotype / phenotype** TT or Tt.

(b) A tall pea plant with the genotype TT is **homozygous / heterozygous** dominant.

(c) A tall pea plant with genotype Tt is **homozygous / heterozygous**.

(d) A dwarf pea plant with genotype tt is **homozygous / heterozygous** recessive.

26. Explain in detail why it is possible for a couple to have four children, all daughters. (3 marks)

27. History relates how King Henry VIII was so desperate to have a male heir that he divorced or disposed of those of his wives who were unable to produce a son.

(a) What sex chromosomes are found in eggs? (1 mark)

(b) What sex chromosomes are found in sperm? (1 mark)

(c) Is it the father's or mother's gametes that determines the sex of an offspring? Explain your answer. (2 marks)

28. There are two types of wings on flies, short or normal. Using the symbol N to represent normal wing, and n for short wing, answer the following questions.

(a) (i) What is the phenotype for a fly that has the homozygous recessive genotype? (1 mark)

....

(ii) Circle the combination that represents homozygous recessive. (1 mark)

NN   **nn**   **Nn**

(b) A heterozygous male fly mates with a homozygous recessive female. Complete the following genetic cross diagram. (3 marks)

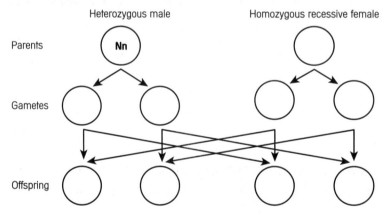

(c) What is the percentage chance of the parents having a short-winged offspring? (1 mark)

....

(Total: .... / 33 marks)

1. Which of the following provides evidence for evolution? Tick the correct option. (1 mark)

Animals ⬭ Fossils ⬭

Plants ⬭ Viruses ⬭

2. Describe **one** way in which fossils are formed. (1 mark)

3. Explain why fossils can be quite hard to find. (1 mark)

4. **(a)** Explain what 'extinction' means. (1 mark)

(b) Give **three** factors that could contribute to the extinction of a species. (3 marks)

(i) _____ **(ii)** _____ **(iii)** _____

(c) Give an example of a species that is now extinct. (1 mark)

(Total: _____ / 8 marks)

Higher Tier

5. New species can arise in a number of ways. Select the **four** correct options. (4 marks)

Isolation ⬭ Asexual reproduction ⬭

Genetic variation ⬭ Natural selection ⬭

Taking cuttings ⬭ Speciation ⬭

(Total: _____ / 4 marks)

1. Cells have to replace substances that are used up, and remove waste products. They do this by osmosis and diffusion. Choose the correct word(s) from the following options to complete the sentence below. (1 mark)

   glucose   **carbon dioxide**   **carbon monoxide**   **oxygen**

   One of the waste products that will diffuse out of a cell is _____.

2. A student investigated the effect of different concentrations of salt solution on the mass of potato chips. The student weighed each one of five chips and then placed each chip into a different concentration of salt solution. After one hour he removed the chips and then reweighed them. The results are given in the table below.

	Concentration of salt solution			
	OM	1M	2M	3M
Mass (g) of chip at start	2.6	2.5	2.6	2.7
Mass (g) of chip after I hour	2.8	2.3	2.1	1.9

   (a) In which concentration of salt solution did the chip gain mass? (1 mark)

   _____

   (b) Complete the following sentence. (3 marks)

   The chip gained mass in this solution because _____ entered the cells through

   the _____ membrane, by the process of _____.

   (c) There is no salt in a OM concentration of salt solution. Why did the student use this concentration? (1 mark)

   _____

   _____

3. Fill in the missing words to complete the following sentences. (3 marks)

   (a) Water and dissolved substances automatically move _____ a concentration gradient.

   (b) They move from a _____ concentration to _____ concentrations.

4. Glucose is reabsorbed into the blood in the kidneys by active transport. Give **two** ways in which active transport is different to diffusion. (2 marks)

   (a) _____

   (b) _____

5. Name **two** substances moved by active transport in the body. (2 marks)

(a) ....

(b) ....

6. Fill in the missing words to complete the following sentence. (2 marks)

Humans have organ systems that are .... to help the ....

of materials.

7. The diagram below shows the villi lining the small intestines in a healthy person.

(a) Describe **two** features of the villi shown in the diagram that help the small intestine to

function efficiently. (2 marks)

(i) ....

(ii) ....

(b) The villi lining the small intestine are also covered in microvilli. Each cell that has microvilli
is packed with lots of mitochondria.

(i) Explain the advantage of microvilli in the absorption of digested food molecules. (2 marks)

....

....

(ii) Why is it necessary for these cells to be packed with lots of mitochondria? (2 marks)

....

....

(c) The villi of a person with coeliac disease are damaged and have a much smaller surface area
compared to the villi of a healthy person.

What effect will this damage have on the function of the small intestine? (1 mark)

....

....

8. Match the numbers on the diagram with the words listed below. Write the appropriate numbers in the boxes provided. (5 marks)

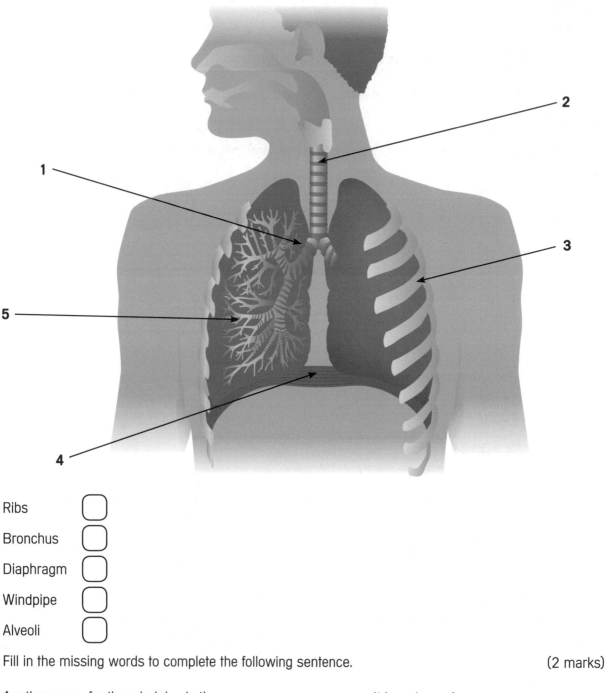

Ribs ⬭

Bronchus ⬭

Diaphragm ⬭

Windpipe ⬭

Alveoli ⬭

9. Fill in the missing words to complete the following sentence. (2 marks)

Another name for the windpipe is the _____. It has rings of _____

to prevent it from collapsing.

10. **(a)** Which substance diffuses from the blood into the alveoli? (1 mark)

....

(b) Which substance diffuses from the alveoli into the blood? (1 mark)

....

11. Which of the following are features of the alveoli? Tick the **two** correct options. (2 marks)

Good blood supply ⬭　　　　No walls ⬭

Thick walls ⬭　　　　Large surface area ⬭

Poor blood supply ⬭　　　　Small surface area ⬭

12. Which **one** gas has a higher concentration in exhaled air than inhaled air? Circle the correct answer. (1 mark)

oxygen　　　　**carbon dioxide**　　　　**nitrogen**　　　　**argon**

13. Emphysema is a lung disease that increases the thickness of the surface of the lungs for gas exchange as well as reducing the total area available for gas exchange.

Two men did the same amount of exercise. One man was in good health, whilst the other man had emphysema.

The results are shown in the table.

	Healthy man	Man with emphysema
Total air flowing into lungs (dm³/min)	89.5	38.9
Oxygen entering blood (dm³/min)	2.5	1.2

(a) Which man has more oxygen entering his blood? (1 mark)

....

(b) Explain why the man with emphysema will struggle to carry out exercise. (2 marks)

....

....

(c) Give **one** reason why someone might develop emphysema. (1 mark)

....

(Total: .... / 38 marks)

1. Explain the function of the circulatory system in animals. (1 mark)

....

2. **(a)** List **three** components of the circulatory system. (3 marks)

....

....

....

(b) Complete the following sentences. (3 marks)

The blood carries .... and .... to all body cells.

The blood carries .... away from all body cells.

3. **(a)** What do we call blood that contains oxygen? (1 mark)

....

(b) What do we call blood that contains carbon dioxide? (1 mark)

....

4. Circle the correct options in the following sentences. (3 marks)

(a) Blood is pumped to the **lungs / stomach / heart / brain** so carbon dioxide can be exchanged for **water / nitrogen / oxygen / mineral ions**.

(b) Blood passes through the heart **once / twice / three times / four times** on each circuit.

5. **(a)** Which type of blood vessel carries blood away from the heart? (1 mark)

....

(b) Which type of blood vessel carries blood towards the heart? (1 mark)

....

6. Give **two** ways in which the composition of blood changes as it travels through the lungs. (2 marks)

(i) ....

(ii) ....

7. Complete the following sentences about capillaries. (3 marks)

Capillaries have .... walls that are one cell thick. This allows substances to easily

be .... into cells of organs. Capillaries are very .... so the

flow of blood through the organ slows down.

8. Match the numbers on the diagram with the words listed below. Write the appropriate numbers in the boxes provided. (4 marks)

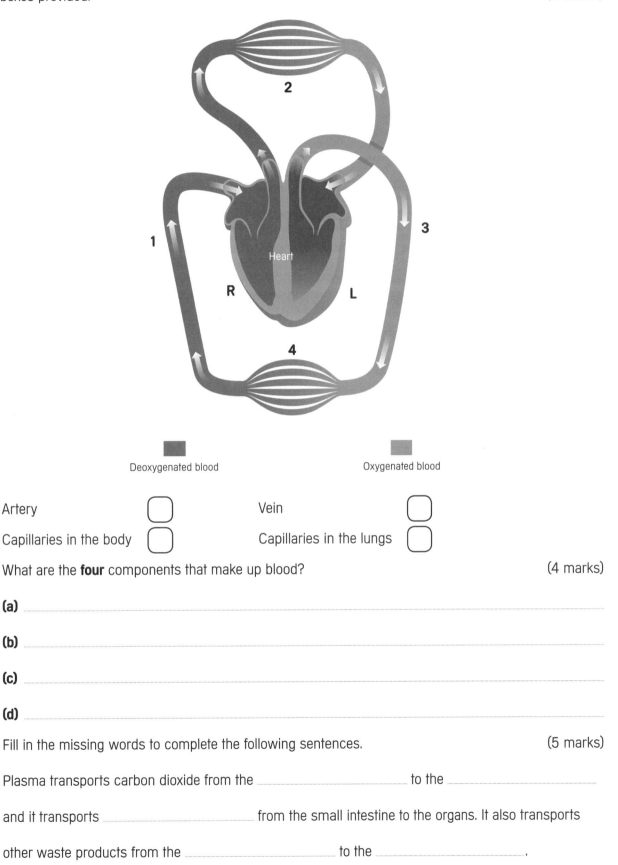

Deoxygenated blood

Oxygenated blood

Artery ⬭

Vein ⬭

Capillaries in the body ⬭

Capillaries in the lungs ⬭

9. What are the **four** components that make up blood? (4 marks)

(a) ....

(b) ....

(c) ....

(d) ....

10. Fill in the missing words to complete the following sentences. (5 marks)

Plasma transports carbon dioxide from the .... to the ....

and it transports .... from the small intestine to the organs. It also transports

other waste products from the .... to the ...., .

11. Fill in the missing words to complete the following sentences. (3 marks)

Red blood cells transport .... from the lungs to the organs. They contain lots

of ...., which combines with oxygen to form ....

12. Complete each sentence about the heart by choosing the correct words below. (3 marks)

an artery   **an atrium**   **a valve**   **a vein**

(a) A ventricle fills with blood by the contraction of ....

(b) When a ventricle contracts, blood is forced into ....

(c) When a ventricle relaxes, the backflow of blood into it is prevented by the closing of

....

13. Plants have two separate transport systems – xylem and phloem. Give the name of the systems responsible for transporting the following: (2 marks)

(a) Transporting water and mineral ions

....

(b) Transporting dissolved sugars

....

14. The roots in plants are covered in root hairs, like the one in the diagram below. (2 marks)

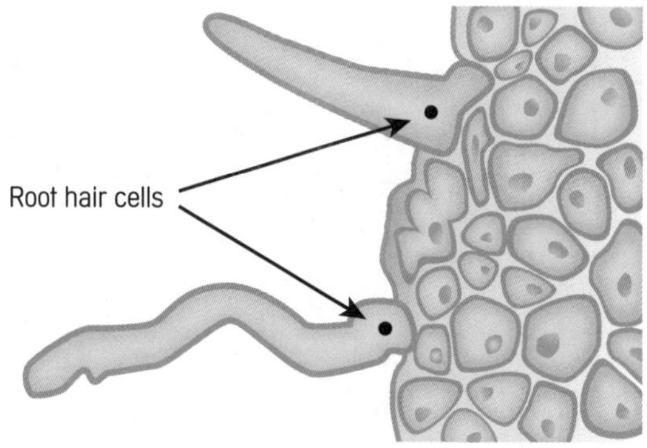

Root hair cells

Explain how root hairs help the plant with absorption.

....

....

....

15. Fill in the missing words to complete the following sentence.

(a) Leaves have a _____ surface area in order to make them very efficient at

photosynthesis. (1 mark)

(b) Most plant leaves are green. List **two** other features common to most leaves. (2 marks)

16. Name the process by which water is **lost** from a leaf. Draw a circle around the answer. (1 mark)

osmosis   transpiration   circulation   diffusion

17. A student investigated the amount of water lost by a plant during different times of the day. The results are given in the table below.

Time	00:00	02:00	04:00	06:00	08:00	10:00	12:00	14:00	16:00	18:00	20:00	22:00
Water lost in cm³	6	5	7	55	105	160	248	230	128	112	8	7

(a) At what time of the day is water lost most quickly? (1 mark)

(b) Give **one** possible reason why water was lost quickly at this time. (1 mark)

18. Apart from light, list the **three** conditions that would increase the rate of transpiration. (3 marks)

(a) _____

(b) _____

(c) _____

19. The diagram below shows the underside of a leaf. (2 marks)

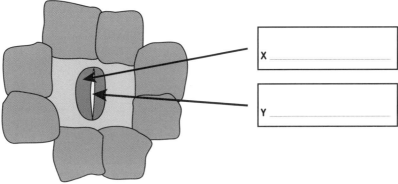

X _____

Y _____

Label X and Y in the diagram.

20. **(a) (i)** In what type of conditions are the stomata open? (1 mark)

....

(ii) What happens when the stomata are open? (1 mark)

....

(b) (i) In what type of conditions are the stomata closed? (1 mark)

....

(ii) Why do the stomata close? .... (1 mark)

(iii) What else stops as a result of the stomata closing? .... (1 mark)

21. A group of students investigated the number of stomata on three different species of plants: X, Y and Z. They estimated the number of stomata per cm^2 on both the upper and lower surfaces of the leaf. Their results are shown in the table.

Plant species	Estimated number of stomata per cm^2 of leaf surface	
	Upper surface	Lower surface
X	0	650
Y	3500	10 000
Z	6000	18 000

(a) (i) Which plant species is likely to grow in a dry region? .... (1 mark)

(ii) Give a reason for your answer. (2 marks)

....

....

....

....

(b) Plants X, Y and Z all have more stomata on the lower surface of their leaves compared to the upper. Suggest how this could help the plants to survive better. (2 marks)

....

....

....

(Total: .... / 63 marks)

1. To function properly, what **five** conditions must the body control levels of?   (5 marks)

    (a) ....

    (b) ....

    (c) ....

    (d) ....

    (e) ....

2. Waste products such as carbon dioxide and urea need to be removed from the body. Circle the correct word in the following sentences.   (4 marks)

    (a) Carbon dioxide is a waste product of **photosynthesis / respiration / transpiration**.

    (b) Carbon dioxide leaves the body through the **skin / lungs / urine**.

    (c) Urea is produced in the **kidneys / liver / lungs**.

    (d) Urea is produced from the breakdown of **glucose / fats / amino acids**.

3. Give **three** functions of the kidney.   (3 marks)

    (a) ....

    (b) ....

    (c) ....

4. When a person's kidneys fail, why does this result in death if left untreated?   (1 mark)

    ....

    ....

5. List **three** substances that are found in urine.   (3 marks)

    (a) ....

    (b) ....

    (c) ....

6. Urea must be removed from the body.

    (a) Which organ makes urea?   (1 mark)

    ....

(b) Which organ removes urea from the body?   (1 mark)

....

(c) What substance is broken down to form urea?   (1 mark)

....

7. What is meant by the term 'selective reabsorption'? Tick the correct option.   (1 mark)

Excess substances are released   ⬭

Water and small molecules are squeezed out of the blood   ⬭

Useful substances return to the blood   ⬭

The kidneys stop working   ⬭

8. The body gains water and ions through food and drink. Fill in the missing words to complete the paragraph below.   (3 marks)

When the .... or .... content of the body is out of balance,

too much water may move in or out of the cells. This process is called ....

9. Fill in the missing words to complete the following sentences.   (4 marks)

(a) In a dialysis machine the blood flows between a .... membrane.

(b) Dialysis fluid contains the same concentrations of useful substances as .... , so

.... and essential .... ions aren't lost through diffusion.

10. Why does dialysis have to be repeated on a regular basis?   (1 mark)

....

11. Is the following statement true or false?   (1 mark)

Kidney transplants are necessary when only one kidney works.

....

12. **(a)** What is the main problem with kidney transplants?   (1 mark)

....

(b) What causes this problem?   (1 mark)

....

(c) Give **two** precautions that could be taken to prevent problems with kidney transplants.　　(2 marks)

(i) ....

(ii) ....

13. Explain why proteins are not present in the urine of a healthy person.　　(1 mark)

14. Complete the following sentence by circling the correct word.　　(1 mark)

After filtration, all the glucose is

reabsorbed.
released.
respired.

15. In which organ is urine stored before being excreted by the body?　　(1 mark)

16. What effect does hot weather generally have on the amount of urine produced? Circle the correct answer.　　(1 mark)

decreases　　**stops**　　**increases**　　**stays the same**

17. Apart from the pancreas, what other organ is involved in controlling blood sugar levels?　　(1 mark)

18. What is one of the causes of diabetes? Tick the correct option.　　(1 mark)

The pancreas does not produce insulin ☐

The liver does not produce glycogen ☐

The kidneys do not remove glucose from the blood ☐

The liver does not produce insulin ☐

19. Diabetics may control their blood glucose by injecting insulin. Apart from using insulin, give one other way diabetics may control their blood glucose.　　(1 mark)

20. Which hormone is produced by the pancreas?　　(1 mark)

B3 | Homeostasis

21. (a) Where are the receptors located that provide information about blood temperature?
Tick the correct option. (1 mark)

Skin ⬭   Brain ⬭

Kidneys ⬭   Lungs ⬭

(b) Circle the correct option in the following sentence. (1 mark)

The normal body temperature is **20°C / 37°C / 75°C / 100°C**.

22. A student in a school football team trained on a hot day and on a cold day. On each day the student did the same amount of exercise by following a programme and drank the same amount of water.

Complete the sentences by drawing a ring around the correct answer.

(a) On a hot day, the student would produce **less / more / the same amount of** urine. (1 mark)

(b) This is because he would produce **less / more / the same amount of** sweat. (1 mark)

(Total: .... **/ 45 marks)**

Higher Tier

23. (a) Describe **three** changes that occur to the body if it becomes too cold. (3 marks)

(i) ....

(ii) ....

(iii) ....

(b) Give **two** changes that occur if the body becomes too hot. (2 marks)

(i) ....

(ii) ....

24. (a) What does insulin convert glucose into? (1 mark)

....

(b) Where is this product mainly stored in the body? (1 mark)

....

(c) What hormone does the body produce that converts the substance from the answer to question **(a)** back into glucose? (1 mark)

....

(d) Where is this second hormone produced? (1 mark)

(e) Describe when this second hormone would be released. (1 mark)

25. The table below compares the air temperature and body temperature of a reptile and a human.

Time	Air temperature (°C)	Human body temperature (°C)	Reptile body temperature (°C)
04:00	11	37	7
08:00	21	37	18
12:00	38	37	12
16:00	36	37	11
20:00	26	37	19
00:00	8	37	8

The human body temperature remains constant throughout the day. Describe **two** mechanisms that occur in the body if the core body temperature is too low. (2 marks)

(a)

(b)

26. A scientist carried out an experiment to see how much sweat and urine a person produced at various temperatures. Before the scientist began his experiment he made a prediction. Complete the following sentences to show his prediction.

(a) (i) As air temperature increases the amount of sweat produced by the body will (1 mark)

(ii) As air temperature increases the amount of urine produced by the body will (1 mark)

(b) Explain your answers to part **(a).** (2 marks)

(Total: .... / 16 marks)

1. The human population has grown over the last 200 years in the UK. This has resulted in damage to the environment. Apart from farming methods, give **two** ways in which humans harm the environment. (2 marks)

   ....

   ....

2. **(a)** *In this question you will be assessed on using good English, organising information and using specialist terms where appropriate.*

   The human population is increasing exponentially. Explain what 'exponentially' means and suggest **two** reasons why the human population is increasing in this way. (4 marks)

   ....

   ....

   ....

   ....

   (b) The human population explosion causes more waste to be produced, which can sometimes be polluting. Give **one** example of how human activity may pollute the following: (3 marks)

   (i) Water

   ....

   (ii) Air

   ....

   (iii) Land

   ....

3. Which of the following gases pollute the air? Tick the **three** correct options. (3 marks)

Oxygen	☐	Carbon dioxide	☐
Methane	☐	Nitrogen	☐
Sulfur dioxide	☐	Chlorine	☐

4. Which of the following are ways that smoke and waste gases from a power station can damage the environment? Tick the **three** correct options. (3 marks)

Cause acid rain	☐	Decrease global warming	☐
Kill trees and plants	☐	Increase carbon dioxide	☐

5. Give **one** example of a living organism that can be used as an indicator of pollution. (1 mark)

   ....

6. Many farmers use chemicals that they spray onto crops growing on their land. Circle the correct word in the following sentences. (3 marks)

(a) To make crops grow larger farmers use **fertilisers / herbicides / pesticides**.

(b) To kill insects that feed on crops farmers use **fertilisers / herbicides / pesticides**.

(c) To kill plants competing with their crops farmers use **fertilisers / herbicides / pesticides**.

7. **(a)** What is deforestation? Tick the correct option. (1 mark)

Planting new trees ☐ Forest fires caused by hot weather ☐

Cutting down large areas of forest ☐ Polluting national parks with litter ☐

(b) Which of the following is caused by deforestation? Tick the correct box. (1 mark)

Decrease in soil erosion ☐

Increase in the amount of carbon dioxide in the air ☐

Increase in rainfall ☐

Increase in habitats ☐

8. Give **two** reasons for large-scale deforestation. **Do not** include the use of wood for timber. (2 marks)

(a) ....

(b) ....

9. What is the name of the gas given off when trees are burned? Tick the correct option. (1 mark)

Carbon dioxide ☐ Oxygen ☐

Methane ☐ Hydrogen ☐

10. Which biological process decreases the amount of carbon dioxide in the atmosphere? Tick the correct option. (1 mark)

Respiration ☐ Exhalation ☐

Photosynthesis ☐ Deforestation ☐

11. (Circle) the correct options in the sentences below. (6 marks)

When deforestation occurs in **tropical / arctic / desert** regions, it has a devastating impact on the environment.

The loss of **trees / animals / insects** means less photosynthesis takes place, so less **oxygen / nitrogen / carbon dioxide** is removed from the atmosphere.

It also leads to a reduction in **variation / biodiversity / mutation**, because some species may become **devolved / damaged / extinct** and **habitats / land / farms** are destroyed.

12. Fill in the missing words to complete the following sentences. (3 marks)

Some .... in the atmosphere prevent .... from escaping

into space. This is called the greenhouse effect.

The greenhouse effect is leading to global ....

13. Name **two** gases that contribute to the greenhouse effect. (2 marks)

(a) ....

(b) ....

14. Which of the following factors contribute to an increase in greenhouse gases?
    Tick the **four** correct options. (4 marks)

    Carbon offsetting ⬚   Deforestation ⬚

    Burning fossil fuels ⬚   A growth in cattle farming ⬚

    Growing rice ⬚   Forest management ⬚

15. Which of the following are the negative effects of global warming? Tick the **two** correct options. (2 marks)

    Climate change ⬚   Erosion of buildings ⬚

    Deforestation ⬚   A rise in sea levels ⬚

    Increase in available land ⬚ Warmer summers ⬚

16. Dylan and Molly investigated the effect of sulfur dioxide on the germination of cress seeds.

The diagram shows their apparatus.

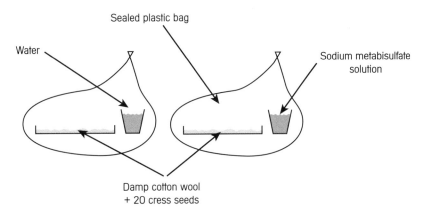

- Sodium metabisulfate solution gives off sulfur dioxide.

- Both bags were left in a warm laboratory for five days.

(a) What was the independent variable in the investigation? (1 mark)

(b) Suggest the main reason for using sealed plastic bags. (1 mark)

Dylan and Molly counted the number of seeds that had germinated after five days. Their results are shown in the table below.

	Number of germinated seeds
Water	18
Sodium metabisulfate	12

(c) (i) What conclusion can Dylan and Molly draw from their results? (1 mark)

(ii) Are their results reliable? Explain your answer. (2 marks)

(iii) Apart from the presence of sodium metabisulfate, list **two** other variables that could have affected the number of germinated seedlings. (2 marks)

* ....

* ....

17. There are a number of ways in which we can help the environment. Draw lines to link the four methods of helping the environment in **list A** to the four corresponding impacts of the methods on the environment in **list B**. (4 marks)

List A

Increasing the amount of metal recycled

Using fewer pesticides and fertilisers

Reducing sulfur dioxide emissions

Increasing the amount of paper recycled

List B

Fewer forests are cut down

Less acid rain is produced

Less pollution of rivers flowing through farmland

Fewer quarries are dug to provide raw materials

18. Organic foods have become popular in recent years. They are grown without the use of pesticides and fertilisers.

A government report in 2007 showed that the production of some organic foods is more damaging to the environment than their non-organic equivalents.

However, supporters of organic farming claim that it is better than non-organic farming in conserving biodiversity and is better for the soil.

(a) What is meant by the term 'biodiversity'? (1 mark)

....

....

(b) Why is it important to conserve biodiversity? (1 mark)

....

....

19. The diagram shows a biogas generator used on a large dairy farm.

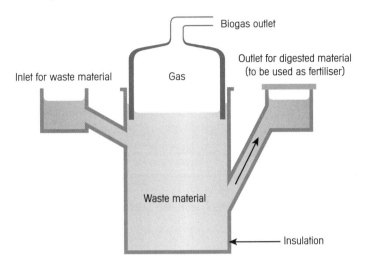

(a) Fill in the missing words to complete the following sentences.   (4 marks)

(i) Biogas mainly consists of ....

(ii) Biogas can be produced by animal or plant .... that contains a lot

of ....

(iii) The insulation helps to keep the waste material at a constant ....

(b) The partially completed table below shows the income and the costs for this biogas generator.

Item	Yearly cost in £	Yearly income in £
Electricity generated from the biogas		26 000
Heating from burning the biogas		3000
Sale of waste after biogas production		7000
Operation and maintenance costs	11 000	

(i) Calculate the yearly profit for this biogas generator. Show your calculations.   (2 marks)

....

....

Yearly profit £ ....

(ii) The biogas generator cost £250 000 to build and set up. Calculate the number of years it will take to pay back the cost of the generator.   (1 mark)

....

Number of years ....

20. For ethanol to be produced from the sugar in sugar cane, which process needs to be used? Tick the correct option. (1 mark)

Aerobic fermentation ⬜   Anaerobic fermentation ⬜

Aerobic distillation ⬜   Fertilisation ⬜

21. Explain what is meant by 'sustainable food production'. (2 marks)

....

....

22. (a) How can we maintain ocean fish stocks? Tick the correct option. (1 mark)

Increase fishing ⬜

Increase fish farms ⬜

Introduce quotas ⬜

Stop eating fish ⬜

(b) Give **one** other method used to help maintain ocean fish stocks. (1 mark)

....

23. (a) What is Mycoprotein made from? Tick the correct option. (1 mark)

A bacterium ⬜   A fungus ⬜

A virus ⬜   A protozoan ⬜

(b) Mycoprotein is made in fermenters. What nutrient is added to help microorganisms grow and reproduce? (1 mark)

....

24. Raising sheep has a greater global warming potential than raising chickens per kilogram of meat produced. Suggest an explanation for this. (1 mark)

....

....

25. The diagram below shows how the energy supplied to a cow is transferred.

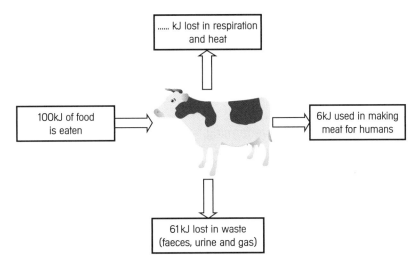

...... kJ lost in respiration and heat

100kJ of food is eaten

6kJ used in making meat for humans

61kJ lost in waste (faeces, urine and gas)

(a) Calculate how much energy is lost in respiration and heat by the cow. Show your calculations. (2 marks)

Amount of energy lost in respiration and heat .... kJ

(b) Calculate the total amount of energy that is lost by the cow. Show your calculations. (2 marks)

Total energy lost by the cow .... kJ

(c) How can the efficiency of meat production in the cow be improved? Tick **two** correct options. (2 marks)

Limit the movement of animals ◯

Heat their surroundings ◯

Allow plenty of space to move ◯

Keep surroundings cool ◯

26. Food that we buy from the supermarket may have been produced by intensive farming methods. There are some people who agree with this method of food production because it is efficient, but there are also people who disagree with such a method because they feel it is cruel to the animals.

(a) Briefly describe what intensive farming of livestock involves. (1 mark)

(b) Give **three** advantages of intensive farming. (3 marks)

(i) ....

(ii) ....

(iii) ....

(c) Give **three** disadvantages of intensive farming. (3 marks)

(i) ....

(ii) ....

(iii) ....

27. Supermarkets are claiming that they are 'reducing their carbon footprints' or trying to be 'carbon neutral'.

(a) Why do supermarkets think that this will attract more customers? (1 mark)

....

....

(b) To help achieve these claims, some supermarkets promote food that has come from British sources. Explain how this can help the environment. (2 marks)

....

....

....

....

28. In the past, bags of compost from garden centres used to contain lots of peat. Explain why peat-free composts are becoming more popular in garden centres today . (1 mark)

....

(Total: .... / 87 marks)

Notes